The Open University

School of
HEALTH
&
SOCIAL
WELFARE

K100
Understanding Health and
Social Care

Block 5

Information, Involvement and Accountability

K100 Production Team

Andrew Northedge (Chair)
Jan Walmsley (Deputy Chair)
Margaret Allott (Course Manager)
Tanya Hames (Course Secretary)
Joanna Bornat
Hilary Brown
Celia Davies
Roger Gomm
Sheila Peace
Martin Robb
Deborah Cooper (VQ Centre)

Jill Alger, Julie Fletcher (Editors); Janis Gilbert (Graphic Artist); Hannah Brunt, Rob Williams (Designers); Paul Smith (Librarian); Deborah Bywater (Project Control Assistant); Ann Carter (Print Buying Controller); Pam Berry (Text Processing Services); Mike Levers (Photographer); Vic Lockwood, Alison Tucker, Kathy Wilson (BBC Producers); Maggie Guillon (Cartoonist)

Regional Education and Training Managers

Lindsay Brigham
Anne Fletcher
Carole Ulanowsky

External Assessor

Professor Lesley Doyal, University of Bristol

This is the K100 core course team. Many other people also contributed to making the course and their names are given in the Introduction and Study Guide.

The Open University
Walton Hall
Milton Keynes MK7 6AA

First published 1998

Designed, edited and typeset by The Open University

Printed and bound in the United Kingdom by Thanet Press Limited, Margate, Kent

ISBN 0 7492 3424 5

For further information on related Open University courses and study packs write to the Information Officer, School of Health and Social Welfare, The Open University, Walton Hall, Milton Keynes MK7 6AA.

1.1

17684B/k100b5u18i1.1

Contents

Study skills by Andrew Northedge

Introduction

Information is probably the most important topic which runs through all the units in this block. Unit 18, which is the first unit, is concerned with information about services and how difficult it can sometimes be to obtain. The reason for this is traced back to the wide variety of organisations that provide health and social care in any locality. Would-be service users, such as Mandy whom you saw in the video scene for Unit 13, often find it difficult to get information about them, and people who work in one service often encounter difficulties in finding out about the others. The 1990s saw the development of co-operation in planning services for a local area, under the terms of the NHS and Community Care Act 1990 and its Northern Ireland equivalent. Among other things, this kind of locality planning does provide greater opportunities for each service to discover what the others do, and to plan together in this light. It has also provided opportunities for organised groups of service users to be involved in the planning and management of the services used by them and people like them. Unit 18 also looks at the way in which service users may be involved in locality planning, and more generally at self-advocacy and the skills this requires.

Unit 19 is about information which is stored in the form of records. It looks at the various functions that recording and documenting may perform in the organisation of health and social care, at the kinds of records that service users and carers need, and the extent to which those who use services can be involved in making the records and controlling the way that information recorded about them is used. One important aspect of this is the confidentiality of information. Unit 19 also looks at confidentiality: at the reasons for keeping information confidential, and the justifications for not doing so under certain circumstances. Unit 21, the 'skills unit' for this block, deals with confidentiality too, and gives you the opportunity to wrestle with the kinds of dilemmas that confidentiality often gives rise to for practitioners.

One of the important functions of recording information is to make people accountable for their actions. Records often say what has been promised, and usually provide evidence of what has or has not been done. Hence they set individuals and agencies up for judgement as to whether they have fulfilled their obligations. Unit 20 is about accountability. It explains what accountability means, looks at the various ways and directions in which people can be accountable, and considers the problems that arise for people when they are made accountable for doing what they are unable to do.

Unit 18
Information and Involvement

Prepared for the course team by Roger Gomm

While you are working on Unit 18, you will need:

- Offprints Book
- Care in the UK
- Unit 3
- Wallchart
- Audio Cassette 5, side 1

Contents

Introduction

This unit is about making services more accessible to people and about involving the people who use services more fully in the design, management and evaluation of the services they use. In this respect this unit picks up and discusses issues you considered in Unit 10. Here the emphasis will be on the important role that information plays in making services more accessible and in the planning of services.

Increasing both accessibility and user involvement has been something that:

- organised groups of service users have campaigned for
- central government has attempted to impose on health and social services
- health and social care organisations have attempted to implement in their own services ...
- ... and to impose on the services they purchase from other agencies.

How far such initiatives have been successful is another matter.

Section 1 sets the scene. It considers the very large number of very diverse agencies in the health and social care field that can be found in any major area of population. It notes how difficult it can be for would-be service users to find out about the existence of these agencies, let alone to discover what they do or whether they are relevant to them. This is something you considered in Unit 13. It also notes that practitioners in health and social care often have similar difficulties. This can limit their ability to give information or advice to clients. Section 1 then looks at the kind of 'information work' that some people in health and social care do, attempting to alleviate this kind of problem.

If people are to access services they need information to do it

However, the complexity and diversity of services is not just a problem of information. It also poses problems of co-ordination. How can the diverse services in a local area co-ordinate their activities one with another? Co-ordination might occur at two levels. At one level all the services dealing with a particular client might co-ordinate their activities in a single, integrated, 'package of care'. Or, at the very least, they might liaise with each other so that each knows what the others are doing. This is the question of how diverse agencies might co-ordinate their activities to meet the needs of Jim and Marianne, the disabled drug users you met in Unit 10. This kind of co-ordination is not dealt with in this unit. However, the role of records and other documents in co-ordinating packages of care is considered in Unit 19.

The other level at which services might be co-ordinated can be called a 'strategic' level. This means co-ordination in *planning* the overall pattern of services for a locality as a whole. Sections 2 and 3 look at what is usually called 'locality planning'. In order to understand this you will need to consolidate what you have learnt already, and learn some more about the way in which health and social care services are organised (Section 2). Locality planning is one of the ways in which organised groups of service users can, and have, become involved in the planning and management of services. To illustrate this there is a case study from the locality planning of community mental health services (Section 3).

Service users need skills to be involved in this way. They also learn skills by being involved. Section 4 looks at the skills of self-advocacy, and to do this uses an audio cassette featuring a self-advocacy group from the field of learning disabilities. It will also consider the differences between advocacy, which you read about in Unit 10, and self-advocacy.

Involvement in locality planning is only one way in which service users can be more involved in the running of the services they use. Section 5 reviews some other ways, but it pays particular attention to the role users of services might play in drawing up the specifications for contracts between purchasers and providers. The same section also considers whether self-advocacy is a always a feasible way for the views of service users to be incorporated into the planning of services, and the circumstances in which other methods might be used in addition, or instead.

Core questions

- Why is it often so difficult to find out about the services available in a local area, and what measures can be taken to improve the quality and dissemination of information about services?

- How do the diverse health and care services in an area attempt to co-ordinate their activities through locality planning?

- How can service users be more fully involved in the planning, management and evaluation of the services they use?

- What skills and what support do service users need in order to be more fully involved?

Section 1

The difficulty in finding out about services

This section looks at the complexity and diversity of services available in a local area and the difficulties this often results in for would-be users of services and for the practitioners who advise them. It sees this problem as one of providing and disseminating information.

As an introduction to this section, think again about Mandy Brown and her son Sean. They were the single-parent family you met in Unit 13. In that unit you practised the skills of assessing their needs, and the needs of some other people. You also considered what kinds of services might satisfy their needs and how it was sometimes difficult to find out about them. These services are scattered around in different agencies, and sometimes in different departments in the same agency. Offprint 23 gives a list of the kinds of services that *might* be relevant to Mandy and Sean in a typical English town. Much the same list could be produced for urban areas in Wales, Scotland or Northern Ireland, but some of the equivalent agencies would have different names. Find Offprint 23 now and look at it. Don't worry for now about the way the list has been laid out. This relates to an activity later in the unit.

Of course, only some of the services listed would turn out to be appropriate for Mandy and Sean, and she and he would only be eligible for some of them. For example, it is most unlikely that the social services department would supply any services (apart from assessment and advice). Sean is merely a poor child, like thousands of others, and not 'disturbed', 'disabled' or abused. But without knowing details about all the agencies on the list it is impossible to decide whether they are worth approaching: impossible for you; impossible for Mandy and for any health or care practitioner trying to help her to access and use the services needed. Remember that this is just a list for Mandy and Sean. The lists for the other people you encountered in Unit 13 would be different.

1.1 Information for service users

In order to access services, would-be users have to be provided with information. Before you proceed further, use Activity 1 to think about the different ways in which information about services might be provided.

Activity 1   **Promoting a service**

Allow about 10 minutes   Imagine you have the task of advertising the services of a new agency. For example, it might be a 'shopmobility' scheme, where motorised scooters are provided in a shopping centre to help people who have difficulty in walking. Or it might be a support group for the informal carers of people with dementia. What *media* could you use to promote the service (pamphlets, newspaper advertisements and so on) and how would you *target* the information – whom would you aim it at, and how would you try to reach them?

Comment   The kinds of media you might have considered include: letters and/or
            phone calls to practitioners and to helplines; entries in directories of
            services and telephone directories; pamphlets; posters; and, if you weren't
            counting the cost, local newspaper, radio and television advertisements.

            However, until you have decided whom to target you cannot decide the
            best way of getting the message to them. On the one hand, you might
            attempt to inform the kinds of people who would use the service or, on the
            other, the kinds of people or agencies who might be in a position to pass
            on the information, such as social workers, health visitors, disablement
            advisers, Citizens Advice Bureaux, and so on. This might include targeting
            venues where potential service users might gather: doctors' waiting rooms
            for example. Since there are rarely any public lists of the people who might
            use a service, but are not actually doing so, your best course of action
            might be to target in the second way. People doing this for real often find
            they have a choice between blanketing an area with publicity, the vast
            majority of it reaching people who don't need it, or closely targeting the
            most obvious points of contact, and then running the risk that some
            potential users – probably the most needy – won't have such a contact
            point. Doing both takes more time and more money.

For your own area you probably know the kinds of places where
information of this kind tends to accumulate: in pamphlet racks and on
notice-boards in libraries, doctors' surgeries, Citizens Advice Bureaux,
or in the council rent office. In such places it is usually not very difficult

This is the right shelf – it says large print books for short-sighted readers!

to find information about 50 or more services; many more if the haul includes directories of services, as it often does. But how many people actually take the information away? Of them, how many read it? And of them, how many act on it? There seems to be very little research about advertising effectiveness for health and social care services. But research from the commercial world is not very encouraging. For commercial flyers and pamphlets, for example, it is generally reckoned that there is one sale for every 3,000 pamphlets distributed (MacIntosh, 1987). And this refers to junk mail carefully targeted according to age, income group and information about purchasing habits, often with incentives such as prize draws and free gifts. When did your social services department last offer you a chance to win a free holiday?

The parallel with commercial advertising is informative. The promotional literature distributed for commercial purposes is usually produced on a generous budget, by people who are expert in researching the market and discovering the kinds of messages that are most likely to grab the consumer's interest and provoke them to action. Apart from nationally mounted health promotion campaigns – about, for example, smoking or HIV – few organisations in the health and social care field can match this. And the experience of health education campaigns is that while they are often effective in changing what people know, they are much less effective in changing what people do (Whitehead, 1989).

Of course, it is important that information about health and social care services directed at possible users is well designed. That means it should:

- be designed for the people who are likely to be using the services

- answer the questions they want answered

- use language they can understand.

The illustration overleaf gives you an example of information produced for people with learning difficulties, in consultation with people with learning difficulties. Lots of people without learning difficulties would find this easier to understand than many other 'official' communications. If you turn to Section 3 of Unit 19 you will see an example of a communication designed for drug users, using a cartoon-strip format. It also seems to meet the three criteria listed above. The same principles extend to making information available in minority languages, in print large enough for people who don't see very well, and in the languages used by people with a visual impairment such as Braille or Moon. And sometimes it might mean having information available on audio or video tape. Some agencies have made great strides in producing information that is accessible and informative (Wiltshire Social Services, 1993; Moffatt, 1993; University of Warwick, 1993).

There is no doubt that the user-friendliness of literature produced by health and care agencies has improved greatly since the 1980s. Much of this is due to the influence of the Campaign for Plain English (Cutts and Maher, 1980), now widely consulted by agencies such as the Benefits Agency and the Inland Revenue, as well as by several NHS trusts. As you saw above, the organisation People First has also played a part in making information easier to understand (People First, 1994). So have other service user groups. Similarly, most large health and care organisations do produce their literature in a variety of languages, although the pamphlets in languages other than English often seem rather difficult to find. The important point here, though, is that, however good the promotional material is, few people seem to read it, and even fewer to act on it.

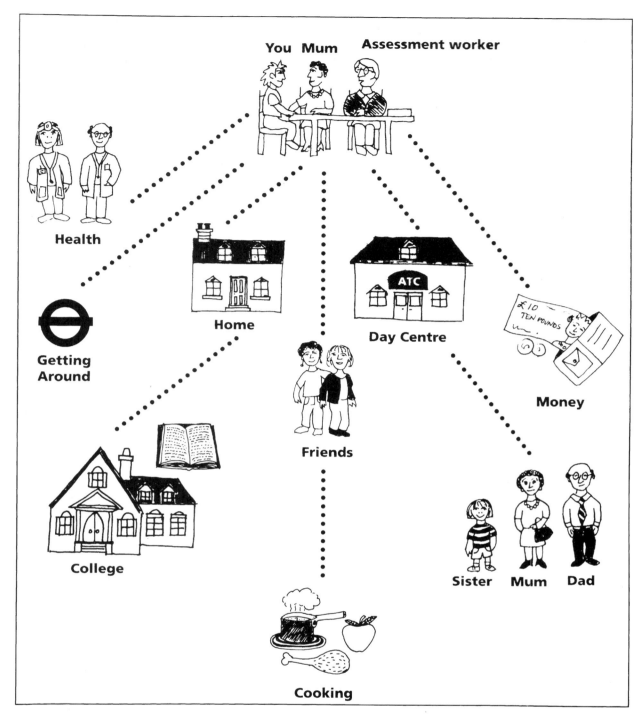

Health

Getting
Around

Home

Day Centre
ATC

Money

College

Friends

Cooking

Sister   Mum   Dad

You Mum   Assessment worker

People First, an organisation of people with learning difficulties, has been very successful in making information easier to understand

---

Activity 2   **Responding to promotional messages**

Allow about 10 minutes   Jot down your ideas about why so few people respond to the information available about health and social care services, or about anything else. You might like to start by thinking of when you last responded to a piece of junk mail, to a poster or something similar, and why you did.

Comment   Assuming that people actually get the information (which is the first hurdle) and would benefit from the service (which is the second), people tend to respond only if *at the time* it is immediately relevant to them. Pamphlets, posters, newspaper advertisements and so on carry 'one-shot' messages. If people don't connect with the message immediately, they rarely take any notice of it, and even if they read it, they tend to forget it quickly. This is one of the reasons for the recent popularity of distributing calendars with information about services round the edges. At least they might stay on the wall for 12 months. This is, of course, why commercial advertisers present the same message hour after hour and day after day on commercial radio and television. In addition, you might have noted that many of the people with whom health and social care services want to connect are upset, confused, depressed, alienated or otherwise not very responsive.

In thinking about how you last responded to some message beamed at you, you might have noted something that has been very well known in the advertising world since the 1940s (Lazarsfeld *et al.*, 1944): people rarely respond to promotional material without discussing this with other people.

Consider someone visiting the chiropodist. She sees a poster advertising a lunch club for people of her age. She would like to get out more and have more people to talk to. But she doesn't know anyone who goes to the lunch club. Would she like the people there? Would they like her? What should she say if she went in? Would she know where to sit? What should she wear? Would she like the food? Are the kitchens hygienic? If she doesn't know the answers to these kinds of questions, she probably won't go. If she has a neighbour she likes who attends the club, then she has a source of information for the questions she needs to be answered. If she goes there she will have a companion.

People need to be able to imagine themselves using a service

In the kinds of close-knit communities described in Unit 11 what services were available was part of the stock of community knowledge. The services may not have been very extensive, but there was always someone who knew what was available at the Miners' Welfare, or the infant welfare clinic, or which dentist inflicted most pain, and which doctor was prepared to waive his fees. There are still communities like this, but many people live outside such networks of information. There is a 'first step' problem here for services that people access themselves. Not many people take the first step unaided.

Serena, who is a carers' support worker, says:

> It can take literally years to persuade someone to come to a support group meeting, and work by me and the CPN [community psychiatric nurse] and the practice nurse, and the doctor and so on. Even if we can arrange for the care of the person [being looked after] then I nearly always have myself to bring the carer to the group. Unless, that is, they are introduced by a friend. Then no problem. And, of course, once they have made the first step then they've got some other people they can go to other things with.

Maureen, who organises monthly outings for housebound older people, says:

> The average length of time it takes is three months. That's two offers refused and the third accepted. But sometimes it can be several years. But then of course it's 'When's the next one?' and it's difficult to strike a balance between giving places to satisfied customers and holding places open for newcomers. Or it's 'Can my friend come?' Or 'I'll only come if my friend comes'. Unfortunately some of the friends aren't disabled or housebound so they're not strictly eligible.

In an entirely different context, John, who works in a drug problem agency, says:

> People don't use the agency as individuals. They join up in groups. So you get sudden influxes of punters. Because one member of the group has sussed it out, all the others come in as well.

These remarks point to something that is fairly common in services such as lunch clubs, carers' groups, outings, recreational facilities, drop-ins and others, which people access of their own volition. The same groups of friends can often be found using a variety of facilities (Brighton Polytechnic, 1992). They learn about them from each other. They value each other's support and company in attending them. In contrast, people who don't have the support of a network often use no such services at all.

All this points to the importance of social networks in carrying information about services and in supporting people to use them (Gottlieb, 1981). In turn it suggests the importance in health and social care of helping people to develop their networks of contacts, and of using the kinds of community development and network-building strategies discussed in Unit 11. Put another way, you can't build communities by showering people with leaflets. It is where there is no community that people are least likely to respond to such information.

> **Key points**
>
> • It is often difficult for would-be users of services to find out about them.
>
> • Information telling people directly about services needs to be well designed to answer the questions they want answered and in a language they understand. It needs to be available at the moment when they need it.
>
> • But, however well designed they are, materials such as pamphlets, posters and advertisements are relatively ineffectual in encouraging people to do things.
>
> • People are more likely to respond to information if it comes from people they know, and if they have their encouragement in accessing services.

1.2 Information for practitioners

The comment for Activity 1 also suggested targeting information about services at the kinds of people and agencies in a position to offer information and advice to potential users of services. This is especially appropriate where services can be accessed only by referral from a doctor, a social worker or some other practitioner. Whether or not services are gate-kept in this way, social workers conducting assessments under the terms of the NHS and Community Care Act 1990, or in Northern Ireland under the terms of the Health and Personal Social Services (Northern Ireland) Order 1991, and in the UK as a whole under the terms of the Carers (Recognition and Services) Act 1995, are supposed to consider and advise clients on a wide range of services: not just those provided by the social services, social work department or health and social services board (Department of Health Social Services Inspectorate/Scottish Social Work Group, 1991; Northern Ireland Office, 1991). Similarly, people like Jim and Marianne, whom you met in Unit 10, might be lucky enough to have a voluntary sector drugs agency in their area, with knowledge about a wide range of appropriate services. The information given by such a practitioner may not be as credible as that given by a relative or a friend with whom the potential service user can identify. However, what practitioners know about services is always available at the time when they meet clients. And when they meet clients may be the time when clients actually need the information.

If you look at Offprint 23 again and the kinds of services that might be relevant to Mandy and Sean, you might guess that such practitioners would also have a problem in knowing the full range of what is on offer. And indeed they do have this problem. Many local authority social services or social work departments employ 'information workers', whose job it is to collect, collate and disseminate information about services. They often find it difficult to discover accurate information about all the services on offer, and the information is soon out of date.

Joyce, for example, is employed by a social services department for five hours a week, for 30 weeks a year, compiling information about health, social care and other services relevant to older people. The other services include travel concessions, travel schemes, educational and recreational facilities, home security advice, and information about the special services of the electricity, gas and water companies. This is for a town with a population of about 80,000. The result is an annual

TRANSPORT

● AGE CONCERN MINIBUS SERVICE

Age Concern Milton Keynes, Minibus Office, 5 Hollin Lane, Stacey Bushes, Milton Keynes. ☎ 01908 - 320387.

Age Concern Milton Keynes has four minibuses with tail-lifts which provide transport for the day clubs, the holiday scheme, shopping trips, outings etc. They are also available for hire by senior citizens and other groups. Details also available from Age Concern, 6 Burners Lane, Kiln Farm, ☎01908 261268

MILTON KEYNES COMMUNITY TRANSPORT

This is a special transport service to frail, elderly and disabled people living in the Borough, who cannot use other public transport.

MK SPECIAL

MK Special provides a wheelchair accessible minibus service for individuals and groups, on flexible scheduled routes

MK FASTCHAIR

The Fast Chair service offers pre-booked wheelchair accessible door-to-door service to individuals or small groups; it travels between the person's home and their destination.

How to book the 'Fastchair' and 'Special'

☎ 01908 321818 Monday to Thursday 8.30 am to 2pm, Friday 8.30 am to 1 pm. Journeys can be booked up to 7 days ahead.

● BRITISH RED CROSS ESCORTS

British Red Cross, District Office, Physiotherapy Unit, Westfield Road, Bletchley, Milton Keynes, MK2 2RA. ☎ 01908 - 370996.

This service provides an escort to accompany an elderly or disabled person on their journey, or to meet them at their departure or arrival point, anywhere in the country.

● BRITISH RED CROSS 'LEND A HAND'

British Red Cross, District Office, Physiotherapy Unit, Westfield Road, Bletchley, Milton Keynes, MK2 2RA. ☎ 01908 - 370996.

This scheme provides a wheelchair pusher for older people and people with disabilities, who would like to go shopping in Central Milton Keynes.

● BRITISH RED CROSS VOLUNTARY DRIVERS SCHEME

British Red Cross, District Office, Physiotherapy Unit, Westfield Road, Bletchley, Milton Keynes, MK2 2RA. ☎ 01908 - 370996.

Provides transport for people of any age, but mainly frail, older or disabled people in or around Milton Keynes. For health appointments, hospital visits and so on, not for shopping or leisure. 48 hours notice is preferred, but more urgent requestswill be considered. The charge is currently 28p per mile, and mileage is charged to and from the volunteer's home.

● DISABLED PERSON'S CAR BADGE (`Orange badge')

If you have permanent difficulties with mobility and your GP supports your application, you may be entitled to a car badge which permits you to park in otherwise restricted areas for a defined time.

You can get a form to apply for a badge from Social Services Department, Rear of Police Station, Stratford Road, Wolverton, Milton Keynes. ☎ 01908 - 835900, or from the Adult Disability ☎01908 835835

Directories of services for particular care groups, like the extracts shown here from a directory produced by the Joint Advisory Group for Older People in Milton Keynes, are difficult to compile, to disseminate to the right people and even more difficult to update

directory of services with about 350 entries. Sponsorship by a national insurance company, with a local headquarters, pays for the printing costs. This allows the directory to be widely available to older people. In practice, however, it is mainly used by social workers, community and practice nurses, sheltered accommodation wardens, housing officers and various voluntary sector advice agencies.

Joyce finds the directory difficult to compile, and it is always out of date to some degree by the time it is published. It is out of date to a greater degree for most of the year.

It is worth considering these problems more closely.

Activity 3 **Solving Joyce's problems**

Allow about 10 minutes

Consider Joyce's problems. Why do you think she has so much difficulty in collecting and publishing up-to-date information? Do you have any suggestions for a better way of going about this task? For this second question think *only* about keeping practitioners and other advisers informed.

Comment

One clue to Joyce's difficulties is given in Offprint 23. Although the offprint refers to services for single-parent families, the same applies to services for older people. There are so many services, provided by so many agencies, most of which are autonomous. There is little problem in obtaining information on the larger providers, but the voluntary sector agencies can be very difficult to find out about. Details such as the times and days of the week on which services are provided and charges for such things as lunches or transport do change quite rapidly. In the voluntary sector, contact addresses can change from year to year. New groups form and established groups collapse. Change is something that should be welcomed if it means that people are continually trying new and better ways of meeting clients' needs.

Another problem arises from the fact that the directory is a printed publication. It has to be a printed publication if it is to be available to the public, but printed publications can only be produced – and more importantly can only be updated – occasionally. If the task were merely to provide information to practitioners, then modern information technology might offer an answer.

For the final years of the twentieth century the state of information technology in health and social services nationally is something of a scandal (Audit Commission, 1995). Some practitioners do not have access to computers at all. Purchasing decisions have often been poorly made so that either the hardware or the software, or both, does not do the job it is supposed to do (Silicon Bridge Research, 1997). The installation of new technology has often been unco-ordinated, so that many hospitals, for example, have several different and incompatible systems which will not communicate with each other. In 1997 long and protracted attempts to create a computer network linking all NHS agencies collapsed (Cross, 1997a, 1997b). It is rare for a social services department to use the same system as its neighbouring NHS trust, and GPs use a wide variety of hardware and software. However, to solve Joyce's problems it may not be necessary to have computer systems that communicate directly with each other. All that is needed is for them all to be able to access the Internet and the World Wide Web. All computer systems can be made to do this.

Public access terminals increasingly offer opportunities for people to access electronically stored information

You probably know a bit about the World Wide Web. If you don't, think of it as a collection of electronic notice-boards – Web sites – which can be consulted by anyone who has a computer, a modem linking it with the telephone system and some relatively simple and cheap software, and on which anyone in the same position can 'post' notices. In fact, these are very sophisticated notice-boards: more like notice-boards with whole books pinned to them, so that the enquirer can find the right book, look at its index and consult the pages of interest (Pierson, 1996).

Hertfordshire Libraries, Arts and Information Web Server

Community Information: Record Details

Organisation Type
    Autism
    Residential Homes for People with Disabilities
    Day Care Services
Name
    Hertfordshire Autistic Community Trust
Alternative Name(s)
    Herts Autistic Community Trust
    HACT
Description
    Two residential homes and one day centre. Based in Bricket Wood and St Albans for adults with autism. HACT is affiliated to the National Autistic Society.
Location
    Bricket Wood
Area
    St Albans
    City and District of St Albans
Address
    Queen Elizabeth the Queen Mother Centre Station Road Bricket Wood St Albans Hertfordshire
    AL2 3PJ
Telephone
    Tel. 01923 678523
Contact
    Elliot, Ms Alison, Principal

A Web page from a local Internet database of health, social care and other services. This example, which comes from the Hertfordshire Library Services 'Infocentre', was one of the pages shown when 'Autism' was selected from the index

In 1997 the Web contained quite a lot of information about health and social services. But it was mainly general information (for example, health promotional information) or about national policies, or specialist information for professionals such as price and dosage information about pharmaceuticals, journal articles of professional interest or campaigning material by pressure groups. But what about the possibilities for using the Internet to handle information about local services? Increasingly, local library services are developing Internet databases on health and social care services which can be consulted by the public or by professionals, in the library or via their own computers, as shown in the Web page illustration.

Think about what Joyce does currently. Apart from publishing an annual directory, she regularly goes through the information files in the social services department, trying to detect out-of-date information, and replacing it with information that is more up-to-date. Other information workers do the same for services for other client groups. The kind of information she is handling is mainly in the form of pamphlets. These take a long time to produce and whoever produces them has to send them to a large number of people, and decide to whom they will send them. By contrast, using an Internet system, a supplier of information has to spend only a few minutes preparing the information, and has to send only one 'copy' to one 'address'. And the supplier of the information is likely to update the information themselves.

Activity 4	**Limitations of an Internet solution**
Allow about 10 minutes	Before you get too enthusiastic, think about the limitations of this solution to the problems of maintaining up-to-date information about health and social care. Jot down your thoughts about this.

Comment   Using the Internet might be an ideal way of keeping practitioners and advice agencies informed, but it would by-pass potential service users who don't have access to information technology. However, there is no reason why other means of conveying information should not be employed for service users in addition to using the Internet for informing practitioners.

Such a solution too might by-pass and marginalise smaller, more informal groups who do not have access to information technology but who none the less provide valuable services and support. However, these are the kinds of organisations that get marginalised under current circumstances. If time could be saved by using the Internet to supply information to those that have access to it, then there would more time to collect and input contributions from agencies that do not have such access. Putting such organisations in a position to *read* the Internet would be a much more difficult problem to solve, although new 'cyber-cafes' seem to open weekly and many public libraries are adding access to the Internet to their other services.

It would not solve the problem of agencies that do not keep others informed about their existence or their activities. Currently, Joyce sends out questionnaires to agencies asking for information. Without repeated telephone calls, many of them don't get returned. New technology won't solve this problem, but it probably won't make it any worse.

Key points

- Practitioners and other people who advise service users also have difficulty in finding out about local services, and providers of local services often find it difficult to tell them.

- New technology offers some solutions to the problems of maintaining up-to-date information about local services.

- To date these opportunities have not been fully exploited.

So far this unit has been about the information that potential users of services might need in order to access services. A particularly important point made in this section has been that people usually make better use of information when they are supported in doing so. The support might come from relatives, friends, neighbours or other people they meet when using services – people like them. And it was suggested that information 'embedded' in the stock of knowledge available to a community or network is usually more accessible and credible than disembodied information in a pamphlet or advertisement. Alternatively, the support might come from practitioners and other professional sources of advice. Here it was suggested that practitioners need to be supplied with up-to-date, easily accessible information and that modern systems of information technology have the potential to do this.

Section 2
Locality planning

The unit so far has been about the information needed to access services. The remainder of the unit will be about the information needed to improve the co-ordination of services and to enable those who use services to play a greater part in determining the way they operate. These two issues are closely connected.

Look again at Offprint 23, the list of services that might be relevant to Mandy and Sean. It suggests a problem apart from the problems discussed above. This is a problem of co-ordination. Most of the agencies listed are autonomous, at least to a considerable degree. They have their own ways of managing their affairs, their own philosophies, their own ways of setting priorities, and their own systems of planning their activities. Put simply, the list gives you a glimpse of a system of health and social care that is very poorly co-ordinated. It is hardly a 'system' at all insofar as the term 'system' implies co-ordination. One of the ways in which the agencies that purchase and provide services attempt to co-ordinate their activities is through what is usually called 'locality planning'. This section is about locality planning and also about how service users can be involved in the process.

2.1 The overall structure of health, social care and other services

In order to understand how the development of services in a local area is planned, you will need to know something about the overall structure of services. For health and social care this is the structure that developed from the NHS and Community Care Act 1990 in England, Wales and Scotland, and from the Health and Personal Social Services (Northern Ireland) Order 1991. As a preliminary, please turn to Care in the UK and look at Figure 1. There is one diagram covering England, Wales and Scotland, and an alternative for Northern Ireland, where services are organised differently.

You will see that the diagram divides agencies into those that are 'purchasers' and those that are 'providers'. Unless you are using the Northern Ireland diagram, it divides them again into 'health' and 'social care' agencies. In Unit 3 you learnt what 'purchasing' means in a health service context. Health authorities issue contracts to NHS trusts and other providers of health care. Fund-holding general practices do much the same, although in Northern Ireland some fund-holders are able to purchase social care services as well (Valios, 1996). Also in Unit 3 you looked at an example of a social services department purchasing home care services from a private sector provider, Independent Nursing Services. Purchasing is sometimes called 'commissioning' and purchasers, 'commissioners'. The Labour government elected in 1997 may end purchasing as such, in the sense of involving money transfers, but it is unlikely to end commissioning, which does not necessarily assume financial transactions. Later in this unit you will learn more about purchasing/commissioning by social services or social work departments.

The diagram then divides the agencies again, according to whether they are 'statutory' agencies or 'independent' agencies. Statutory means established by Act of Parliament. The term 'authority', as in 'health authority', always indicates a statutory agency. Independent agencies include voluntary or 'not-for-profit' agencies *and* 'private' agencies, which are often, although not always, enterprises that are run to make a profit. There are many kinds of independent agencies that are neither quite 'voluntary' nor quite 'private', and general practices and NHS trusts are neither quite 'independent' nor quite 'statutory'. However, independent agencies are only very rarely 'purchasers' of services and then only on a small scale. When the term 'purchaser' is used it usually refers either to a fund-holding general practice or to a local authority social services or social work department, a health authority (or health 'board'), or, in Northern Ireland to the health and social services authorities/boards. It all sounds very complicated because it *is* complicated.

Activity 5   **What fits where?**

Allow about 10 minutes

To help you to flesh out the bones of what has been said above, try mapping the *health* and *social care* agencies listed in Offprint 23 on to the diagram in Care in the UK. The list in the extract has been laid out to make this easy for you. Then focus on Gingerbread, a national organisation with local branches offering information, advice and support to single-parent families, which lobbies for their interests nationally with central government and locally with the statutory agencies. First, where does Gingerbread fit on the diagram? Second, the local branch might raise all its money from its own members, from fund-raising events, from charitable contributions from individuals, from other charities (such as the National Lottery Charities Board) or from company donations. But how else might it earn an income locally?

Comment   You should have had little difficulty in locating Gingerbread on the diagram. It is on the social care side. It is a voluntary agency and a 'provider' not a 'purchaser' of services. It is on the right-hand side of the diagram towards the bottom (English, Welsh and Scottish version).

The local branch might receive no financial support at all from the statutory agencies, but it might receive a grant from them, or it might have a contract with the social services department to provide, say, a single-parent families resource centre, being paid a fee for this.

Just to clear up a possible source of confusion, there is really no clear distinction between grants on the one hand and contracts on the other. The term 'contract' implies a more closely defined set of conditions, which Gingerbread would have to follow in order to go on receiving the money. And, for example, the National Lottery Charities Board says it gives 'grants'. But its agreements with the organisations to which it gives money look very much like 'contracts'. They are indeed contracts in the legal sense of the term: that is, promises enforceable at law.

The diagrams in Care in the UK were designed to cover only those services that are most obviously 'health' and 'social care' services. But, thinking of Mandy and Sean again, there are many agencies that fall outside this narrow definition, which are none the less relevant to their health and welfare. These are listed in the third column of Offprint 23. For example, housing seems to be more important for Sean's health than anything provided through the 'health service'. Income from the Benefits Agency is perhaps the most important basis for their health and welfare currently. The Child Support Agency is likely to enter Mandy's life soon if it has not done so already. Education and training might well improve her prospects. Mandy is likely to be a candidate for the new Welfare to Work programme, which will provide her with childcare while she works or trains. Some education and training providers offer counselling for personal problems, some provide accommodation, and some in the private sector even provide some health care for trainees.

So health and social care needs are met not only by what are usually thought of as 'health' and/or 'social care' agencies. In fact, for a very large percentage of the population, the most important services sustaining their health and social welfare lie outside the orbit of the NHS and the social services departments. The important point here is that when it comes to planning the health and care services for a local area a wide range of agencies needs to be involved. If you wanted to convene a meeting to review and make recommendations about services for, say, single-parent families in an area, you would probably want to invite representatives from all the agencies listed in Offprint 23. But some single-parent families have members with disabilities, some include members with mental health problems, some are from minority ethnic backgrounds, some include members who have broken the law or have problems with illicit drugs or alcohol. You can see that the set of organisations you might consider inviting to your meeting is growing larger. You would need a spacious venue to include them all.

Key points

- People's health and welfare depend on a great many services that are not 'health' or 'social care' services in a narrow sense.

- The health and social care services needed by one person may be very different from those needed by another.

- Therefore, when it comes to planning for the health and social welfare of a locality, a very large number of agencies have to be involved.

2.2 Locality planning for health and social care

Under the NHS and Community Care Act 1990 local authority social services and social work authorities have a legal duty to draw up and annually review plans for the *social care* aspects of community care – so-called 'community care plans'. The health and social services boards in Northern Ireland have similar responsibilities. You considered one such plan in relation to Jim and Marianne in Unit 10 and you will be taking a closer look at another later in this unit. These plans have to be produced in consultation with the relevant health authorities and representatives of service users. Although it is not a statutory requirement, government guidance makes it clear that other interested parties should be consulted. These include the housing authorities, the transport authority, the education authority, the police authority and the probation authority, the providers of health or social care such as NHS trusts, GPs and independent residential and nursing homes, and the various voluntary agencies.

Under the same legislation health authorities have a legal duty to plan *health services* for their area, again in consultation with other agencies. Through the 'Local Voices' initiative of 1992 (National Health Service

Management Executive, 1992, 1995; National Association of Health Authorities and Trusts, 1993) the government imposed an additional duty on the health authorities to draw up their plans in consultation with the public. Fund-holding GPs have to draw up annual 'business plans'. Although they do not have to consult with their patients, some do, and their spending plans have to accord with that of the health authority. The new Labour government elected in 1997 intends that GPs should take a more central role in local health and social care planning, but the need for co-ordinating the planning of large numbers of agencies will remain.

In practice, health authorities and local authority social services and social work departments often use the same processes of consultation to produce, on the one hand, the 'community care plans' for social care and, on the other the annual 'locality commissioning' or 'locality purchasing plan' for health services (Smith and Shapiro, 1997). The same structure is often used as well by the local housing authorities to draw up their annual 'housing investment plan' (HIP), which is important for special needs housing, sheltered housing, and housing built for low-income families. Through the same structure the housing associations in England and Wales often gain the support they need from other authorities for their applications to the central government agency that funds housing association building. Often the whole process is called 'locality planning', combining planning for health, social care, public housing and sometimes other needs as well.

However, planning for housing, or indeed planning to provide a new hospital, in turn has to be linked with the local authorities' planning for industrial, retail and residential development, conservation, roads and public transport: the so-called 'structure planning' that local authorities are required by other legislation to do. There is another planning structure for drug and alcohol education and services, initiated by the

government White Paper *Tackling Drugs Together* (1995). Providing services for people with drugs or alcohol problems, like Jim and Marianne, involves action by social services and the health service, so these plans have to be built into the community care and locality commissioning plans. Both the local education authorities and the Training and Enterprise Councils/Companies (Training and Employment Agency in Northern Ireland) have their own planning procedures for education and training respectively, which bump into the planning structure for health and social care.

From 1996 onwards social services departments in England and Wales have had a statutory obligation to draw up and annually review a children's service plan for child welfare and child protection. Again, this is planning that has to be done in consultation with other agencies, and is sometimes done through the same structures as are used to produce the community care plan (Sutton, 1995; Thompson, 1996; Hudson, 1997).

All these different plans have to be submitted to central government for approval. In addition, planning services means planning budgets. So all this planning has to be conducted within the context of financial management plans, which, in the case of local authorities, cover expenditure on services in addition to health and social care. For example, the elected members of a local authority may find themselves having to decide between expenditure on the fire service and expenditure on care of the elderly; or between expenditure on education, or roads, or street lighting, or police vehicles and expenditure on support services for people with mental health problems.

Just to add to the complexity, in various parts of the UK there are projects funded by the World Health Organization (WHO), European Union and/or central government that are designed to bring agencies into closer relationships with each other. These include the WHO 'Healthy Cities' projects (Davies and Kelly, 1993) throughout the UK, the 'Action City' schemes in Northern Ireland (McShane, 1993), the English Department of Health (1994a) 'Healthy Alliances' programme, the English Department of Health and Department of the Environment (1995) 'Building Partnerships' programme and the Welsh 'Communities for Better Health' programme (Health Promotion Wales, 1994). By the time you read this there will be other kinds of local partnership scheme deriving from the Labour government elected in 1997. Where such schemes are in operation they have an impact on the locality planning process.

All this is a way of saying that planning for health and social care is complex and difficult. Not only is it difficult for outsiders to understand, but the people whose job it is find it difficult too.

None the less, in the abstract the planning process is easy enough to understand. One way of looking at it is in terms of Figure 1 (overleaf).

In looking at Figure 1 note that 'planning' is not just something that happens in advance and then stops. It should be something that goes on all the time as information becomes available through the experience of delivering services.

The important questions for planning are relatively simple to ask. They are questions A to D on Figure 1. The answers, however, may be very difficult to find, and for two main reasons. The first is the magnitude and complexity of the task. The second is the fact that this is a highly political process in the sense that the different agencies involved may well have competing interests. Just look at question C. There are always

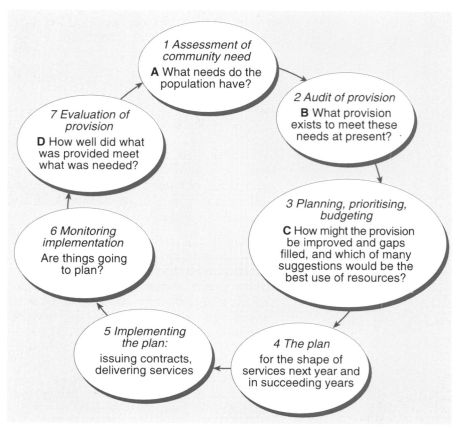

Figure 1
The planning process in health and social care

many competing suggestions for spending the same limited amount of money. Different alliances of interests involved in the planning process may support different proposals for expenditure.

It is important to appreciate the scale and the complexity of this planning. For example, the community care plan for the county of Hertfordshire covers a population of just over a million people, and refers to social services expenditure of around £195 million (1997/98). The lead agency for community care planning is the county council as a social services authority. But the plan has to be drawn up in consultation with the county's own education, probation, police and trading standards authorities, two health authorities, about 125 general practices, seven NHS trusts, eight district councils, which are the housing, environmental health and public transport authorities, and 12 housing associations, which provide special needs housing. At a rough estimate there are around 200 residential and nursing homes that are supposed to be consulted and about 7,000 voluntary sector organisations in the health and social care field. Planning for health care involves much the same agencies, but much more money.

In Hertfordshire, as is common elsewhere, there is a very complex hierarchy of planning committees, with widespread involvement from other agencies, and there are also open public consultation meetings. In some areas, however, the 'general public' are consulted using social survey techniques – questionnaires administered to representative samples of the general public (Bowling, 1993). Other areas use focus groups or 'citizen juries' (Bromley Health, 1995; Brindle, 1995; Ogden, 1996). These are small groups of people chosen to represent the different kinds of individuals who live in the area, who are asked to choose between different options for the development of health and social care services – although their decisions are not the last word on what is actually planned for. In yet other areas the 'general public' doesn't seem to be consulted at all.

The other major player in the game is central government. No representatives of central government are involved at local level but planning has to be conducted within financial limits, which are largely set by central government, according to central government timescales. Each year usually brings some new legislation, or some new central government guidelines that have to be implemented in the plans for next year, or new centrally imposed performance targets that local services are supposed to meet. The Patient's Charter is the source of some of these performance targets for health, and you will consider these in more detail in Unit 20.

It should be obvious that this kind of planning cannot be done through a few quick meetings involving a handful of people. Rather, it is a process that goes on all the time, and year after year. Within an area the size of a county council, a metropolitan borough or a unitary authority, or, in Northern Ireland, the area covered by one of the health and social services boards, thousands of people will have some input into the plans, some unwittingly. For many, this is simply an aspect of their work as managers or practitioners in health or social care, providing routine information about the jobs they do. For other people, collecting information, convening meetings, negotiating agreements and writing reports for planning purposes is a full-time job. You will be looking at one such job in more detail later.

To produce the plans it is necessary to break the process down into manageable pieces. First, not everyone can be consulted, so it is necessary to create representative structures: for example, one GP may represent all the practices in an area, or a representative of a federation of residential homes may represent all of these, or there may be an electoral system through which the large number of voluntary groups elect people to represent the voluntary sector as a whole. Second, planning is often done separately for different care groups – for older people, people with physical difficulties, children and families, people with mental health problems, and so on. And, third, it is done by breaking down large areas into smaller planning localities. Thus, for example, although the community care plan for Hertfordshire is published for the county as a whole, it is a compilation and reconciliation of plans for smaller areas. This has the advantage of allowing planning to be sensitive to the particular needs of different localities and to increase the numbers of people and agencies that can be involved in the process.

As noted, planning is also made difficult by the fact that the different agencies involved may well have competing interests. Resources are finite, so health authorities may prefer schemes for community care that minimise their expenditure and maximise expenditure from social services, or vice versa. You encountered one such area of dispute in Unit 3. This was about whether the health service or social services should be responsible for 'continuing care'. Again, what organised groups of service users say they want may be quite different from what health and care practitioners think they need. Voluntary organisations may be in direct competition with each other for grants or contracts and, for example, finance flowing towards the voluntary sector in the mental health field is finance not flowing towards the voluntary sector in the field of physical disabilities. Often, the planning process involves local authorities that are controlled by different political parties: a housing authority under Conservative control facing a social services authority under Labour control. In Northern Ireland the sectarian divide makes matters even more difficult, although here, for this same reason, democratically elected councils are not responsible for housing or social services, unlike in the rest of the UK.

Against all this complexity there is one thing that simplifies the planning process: only minor changes can be made from year to year. At the beginning of each planning year, well over 90 per cent of expenditure for health and social care is already allocated, often for several years ahead. It is tied up in permanent posts, in grants or contracts lasting a year or more, in buildings, in equipment and in loan repayments. Planning at local level, then, tends to centre on how to spend the 5 per cent or so of the budget that is not already determined. In the mid-1990s planning was as much about deciding what to protect against cuts as it was about what to spend extra money on.

For the health authority, social services authority and fund-holding practices, the planning process answers the question 'What shall we purchase next year?' But it does more than this. By bringing together a wide range of interests in health and social care it enables each to learn about the others. Even if no money is involved it often allows for two agencies to develop schemes in partnership with each other, or avoids two agencies investing their efforts in ways that duplicate each other. In addition, the planning process generates a great deal of documented information about local needs, about who is doing what, about what works and about what doesn't.

Key points

- Locality planning usually refers to the process of making forward plans for health services, social care services, and sometimes other services as well.

- Social services and social work authorities have a legal obligation to draw up and annually review a community care plan, and health authorities have a legal obligation to draw up annual health purchasing or locality commissioning plans.

- Both often use the same machinery for consulting with a wide range of interests.

- Locality planning offers opportunities for those involved to learn about each other's services.

- It also offers opportunities for organised groups of service users to be involved in the planning of health and social care services.

- Locality planning is a very complex and often a highly politicised activity in so far as it brings together groups with different interests who compete for the same limited resources.

2.3 What is in the plans and how does it get there?

The discussion so far has been rather abstract. A case study will bring it to life. The case study shows how it was decided that a health authority and a local authority social services department together would 'purchase' a 'resource centre' (day centre) for younger people regarded as having 'severe mental health problems': the Phoenix Centre. Since this is a day centre run by the users themselves – who prefer to be called 'survivors' – health and social services are purchasing a service from the users themselves. A brief description of the Phoenix Centre is given in the case study box. The case study is a fiction, but is closely based on two similar projects in two different areas.

The Phoenix Centre

The Phoenix Centre is a facility for young adults (aged 17–30) who have been diagnosed as suffering from severe mental illness and are living in the community. It is located in a small industrial unit, converted for the purpose near the town centre. During the day, and on some evenings, it functions as a 'drop-in' or social centre, with coffee bar, pool table, television and video recorder and other leisure equipment. It also serves as a base for the campaigning activities the members do in their attempts to improve services for people like them. And it serves as a base from which members can telephone social workers, the Benefits Agency and other organisations from which they receive services. There is a word processor and printer, telephone, fax and other office equipment.

Organised activities at the centre vary according to demand, but have included an art group, photography, making a 'video diary' and improvised drama. Some of the members also use the centre for music practice. Acupuncture is available once a week. The 'counselling room' can be used for interviews between clients and community psychiatric nurses, social workers, counsellors or probation officers – although some members prefer to make a clear distinction between what happens in the centre and 'treatment'.

The centre has a management committee constituted by all the 'members', although it is a little unclear as to what 'membership' means, except turning up to the centre. A senior social worker, the voluntary sector mental health development co-ordinator and a retired business executive who manages the money also attend management committee meetings. None of these three has a vote. In practice a small core of centre users take most of the decisions.

There is a full-time, paid, centre 'organiser' who was interviewed and appointed by the members. Since he is on the premises for 37 hours a week or more, he is inevitably very influential in determining what goes on. Nominally, however, he is the employee of the centre users. He experiences frequent conflicts between what centre users ask him to do and what he thinks he should do.

Attendance at the centre is sporadic, but in the daytime, from the late morning onwards, two or three members are usually present, and sometimes many more. Currently attendees are drawn from a pool of around 17 people. They are all white, and all male. Like many facilities for people diagnosed as having severe mental illnesses, this one is crisis-prone, reflecting the mental health crises of members, and sometimes conflicts of personality between them. Drug and alcohol use on the premises is banned, but sometimes people arrive at the centre 'high' on drugs or alcohol. Users who are evicted from their homes present a particular problem. When this happens – which is often – there is a demand to use the centre for overnight accommodation. Members vacillate between accepting this and resenting anyone turning 'their' centre into a residence. People who are violent on the premises are suspended from attending. But sometimes getting them to leave can be difficult. The centre has a policy of not involving the police. The centre organiser has been advised by his union that he cannot be required to follow such a policy.

The centre is financed through contracts between the management committee and social services and the health authority. The premises were made available at a token rent by the district authority. Refurbishment, furnishing and decoration were paid for by donations from local firms. The office equipment was donated in kind by local companies through the local community trust, which acts as a conduit for much local company giving. Some of the organised activities at the centre are provided by a community arts project, financed by the regional arts council, the district council, and the National Lottery Charities Board. Acupuncture is provided by students in training from a local complementary medicine centre. The Phoenix Centre pays only for the needles used.

The Phoenix Centre is now up and running. But what planning went into it? How did it get into the community care plan of the social services department and the locality commissioning plan of the health authority? An extract from the community care plan for the area, in the year before Phoenix opened, will give you some clues. Again, this is a fictionalised version of several real documents. It appears as Offprint 24.

Activity 6

Allow about 20 minutes

Phoenix: a place in the plan

Find Offprint 24 'Locality plan for Slegborough District: mental health 1996–7'. It represents the kind of synopsis that is often produced as an adjunct to the plan proper, sometimes as a précis of the plan as a whole, and sometimes, as in this case, as a précis of only a small part of the plan. This is for the obvious reason that community care plans are large documents, few people want to read every section, and authorities don't want the expense of circulating more information than people actually need.

For this activity simply read the 'plan' and ring, underline or highlight those parts of it that you think are most relevant to financing a user-run day centre for younger people with severe mental health problems.

There will be no comment for this activity. You will see which parts are most relevant as the story of the Phoenix Centre unfolds.

Making a case

Getting some new provision built into the locality plans means making a persuasive case for it. That means mobilising information, and using it in an argument that will be convincing to the many people who have to be convinced. In effect it means providing compelling answers to the lettered questions in Figure 1. Sometimes this is true also of making a case to argue against cutting a particular service.

Activity 7   Sources of information for planning

Allow about 15 minutes

The four questions in the grid below are the lettered planning questions from Figure 1.

(a)   Look again at Offprint 24 and see if you can find examples of answers to each of these questions in the extract from the locality plan.

(b)   Then see if you can guess what kind of information was used to answer the question.

For example, the locality plan refers to the excess case loads of mental health practitioners. This relates to the question 'How well did what was provided meet what was needed?' And the answer is: 'Not very well'. The information about case loads comes from the routine monitoring of employees' work. What 'excess' means comes from a comparison with other areas. Audit Commission research is mentioned as the relevant source of information here (Audit Commission, 1994).

Use the grid below for your answer.

Question	Example of answer in Offprint 24	Information from
A What needs do the population have?	Improve Services for people with drug + alcohol problems, in line with the 'Tackling Drugs Together' initiative.	Central Government initiative.
B What provision exists to meet these needs at present?	Noted availability of acute psychiatric ward.	Hospital – budget cuts.
C How might the provision be improved and gaps filled, and which of many suggestions would be the best use of resources?	Additional drug worker.	
D How well did what was provided meet what was needed?		

Comment | Your answer to part (b) of the question will depend on which examples you chose. You probably won't have used the same classification as appears below, but see if you can marry up your answers with the following.

Information from research

The information may have come from research conducted *elsewhere*, with the results being applied to the local area: for example, an estimate of the number of people who will be experiencing severe mental illness in the local area may be derived from research conducted in similar areas elsewhere. In Offprint 24 note the reference to national research that is used to estimate how many cases of severe mental illness might be found in the local Urdu-speaking community.

Alternatively, the information may have come from research conducted in *the local area*: for example, a local survey of the problems experienced by the informal carers of people with severe mental health problems. In Offprint 24 note the reference to local research: *Provision for Community Mental Health*.

Service or management information

This is information collected *in the course of delivering a service*. Examples include ethnic or gender monitoring information; numbers of people entering hospital for psychiatric treatment; numbers of places available in supported housing.

It can include budgetary information about how much money is available, what it can legally be spent on and how much particular services cost.

Benchmarking information

This is information about *what services elsewhere achieve,* against which services in this area can be compared. The point of having performance indicators is to enable the performance of the same kinds of agencies in different areas to be compared and judged. In Offprint 24 note the reference to the Audit Commission, which produces a great deal of benchmarking information.

Information for making financial comparisons is also important here.

Opinions

Opinions may be about preferences, priorities, quality, acceptable levels of expenditure, and so on, and may be those of:

- service users
- local politicians
- managers and practitioners
- campaigning and lobbying groups
- the general public.

Such opinions might be collected systematically by conducting research (see above) or allowed to influence planning because the people with the opinions are involved in the planning process. The locality plan itself involves the views of all these groups because they have been involved in the planning process.

The case for getting the Phoenix Centre included in the locality plans involved all the types of information listed above. The need for such a centre was estimated on the basis of national statistics and research conducted elsewhere on how many people aged under 30 in the area might be diagnosed as having a 'severe mental health problem' (Meltzer *et al.*, 1995). Service information from the NHS trust showed how many people in this age group per year were treated in the acute psychiatric ward, and the managers of the two local community mental health teams gave estimates of how many people might be likely to use such a centre. Service information was also used in order to cost the project. Benchmarking information came from reading published articles about the successes, and the failures, elsewhere in setting up user-controlled day centres and similar facilities (Lindow, 1994, for example). The initiative for the Phoenix Centre derived originally from the opinions of a group of younger adults, diagnosed as having severe mental health problems, who were using an existing day centre that was run on very traditional and rather authoritarian lines and that catered for all age groups.

In the consultation process the opinions of the local branches of MIND, the National Schizophrenia Fellowship and MINDLINK (an organisation run by service users under the MIND umbrella) were influential in supporting the project. An organisation for the carers of people with severe mental health problems was against the project. So was a local society providing services to older people with dementia, since it competed for funding with their own plans for providing respite care for the carers of confused older people. A local councillor from the borough council – not the same council that runs the social services department – lobbied the county councillors of her own party in favour of the project. The probation service representatives were very supportive of the project. Some of their clients were on psychiatric probation orders. Support also came from the local drug addiction agency since several people with mental health problems used their office as a drop-in centre, and the drug agency didn't think they were appropriate clients for them. That support entered the community planning process through its overlap with the process for planning drug and alcohol services. The GPs had no opinion one way or the other. The social services team leaders for mental health were in favour. The other social workers, the community psychiatric nurses and the staff at the day centre whom the 'survivors' were critical of, were not asked.

The hand of central government can also be detected in the process. If you look again at Offprint 24 (the locality plan) you will see that it starts by declaring some priorities for service development. The important one for the Phoenix Centre is 'to extend the range of community provision for people with severe mental health problems'. You probably identified this as relevant in your response to Activity 6. This priority was not dreamt up locally but was set by central government for both the health authorities and the local authority social services departments (Department of Health, 1990, 1995). The important point here is that in locality planning the most persuasive arguments are those that are in line with previously established priorities. You will notice how the plan records progress in terms of meeting priorities set in previous years. You may have been aware that 1997 was national carers' year, and the plan reflects this also. The high profile given in the plan to drug problems also reflects a central government initiative (*Tackling Drugs Together*, 1995). Making a case for a particular kind of provision is even more persuasive if it matches priorities that are backed with earmarked moneys from central government. For the social services department the prioritising of 'the most severely mentally ill' was backed up by some additional money from central government, the Mental Illness Specific Grant, to be used in meeting these priorities (Department of Health, 1994b), and a one-off increase in funding for local authorities for spending on mental health in 1996–97 (Department of Health, 1996). In this sense the proposal for the Phoenix Centre had a good chance of being successful.

Key points

- Information is crucially important in the locality planning of services.

- It doesn't determine what is planned for, but it does feature in the debates between interest groups favouring one scheme or another.

- Important information includes:
  - the results of research conducted elsewhere applied to the local area
  - the results of local research – about needs, about 'consumer satisfaction' or evaluation studies of the quality of provision
  - service information collected as part of the routine process of delivering care: for example, about numbers of clients using a service, or ethnic monitoring data
  - benchmarking information – about how things are done in other places
  - financial information – what services cost, how much is in the budget
  - information about the amount of support a particular proposal has, and from whom
  - information about current central government priorities.

However, none of this really tells you much about how the Phoenix Centre came about. How was it that the ideas and aspirations of a smallish group of young adults, often showing what others would regard as bizarre behaviour, progressed from their moans and groans about existing provision to become a fully-fledged and funded project managed by themselves? From reading through the key points, you may already have identified one of the problems: the difficulty that a small organisation might have in mobilising a case for some new provision. So what kind of support is available? To answer this question it is necessary to look in more detail at the jobs of people who support the planning and consultation process.

Section 3
Supporting service users in locality planning

There are people employed in the health and social care sectors whose jobs are partially or totally concerned with trying to pull together the activities of the various agencies. They don't deliver health or care services, but act as go-betweens, conveying information here and there, convening meetings, brokering agreements, and organising presentations and consultation events. As an example, this unit will consider the job of a *voluntary sector mental health development co-ordinator.* Don't worry about the title. Similar jobs relating to mental health, disabilities, elderly care, or services for minority ethnic groups, and so on, go under a wide variety of titles. What they have in common is that they are jobs that are done in the spaces between agencies, with the aims of:

- improving co-ordination between services
- supporting the planning process
- increasing the extent to which those who use services can influence their planning and delivery.

3.1 Planning and the voluntary sector

Usha Ayer is the (fictional) voluntary sector mental health development co-ordinator who played an important part in establishing the Phoenix Centre. She is introduced in the next box.

Introducing Usha Ayer

One of the real people on whom the character of Usha is based says: 'No one really understands the job I do and the title doesn't help very much'. In Usha's job title 'voluntary sector' means, first, that an important part of her job is stimulating and supporting voluntary sector initiatives in the mental health field, including those organisations run by people who use mental health services or have used them in the past.

Second, it means that she is placed in a voluntary sector agency – a council for voluntary services (CVS). This is a local umbrella organisation for local voluntary sector agencies. Among other things, in this area the CVS organises elections among voluntary sector organisations to determine who will represent them at higher levels of the locality planning system. In another area a post like Usha's might have been placed in a local branch of a national mental health charity, such as the National Schizophrenia Fellowship, the Alzheimers Disease Society, MIND (in England or Wales), the Scottish Association for Mental Health (SAMH) or the Northern Ireland Association for Mental Health (NIAMH). In yet another area there might not be a post like Usha's at all.

Despite the word 'voluntary' in the job title, the money for Usha's post comes from the statutory services. Half comes from the local health authority and half from the local authority social services department. The majority of funds for 'voluntary sector' activities in health and care actually *do* come from statutory services. 'Voluntary' refers to management and control rather than to the source of funding. CVSs are run by unpaid management committees whose members are usually, as in this case, employees, management committee members, volunteers or service users of other voluntary sector agencies, or workers or managers or service users from statutory services, plus some people who are just there as interested members of the public. Figure 2 shows how the management committee members of Usha's CVS relate to other organisations in the area.

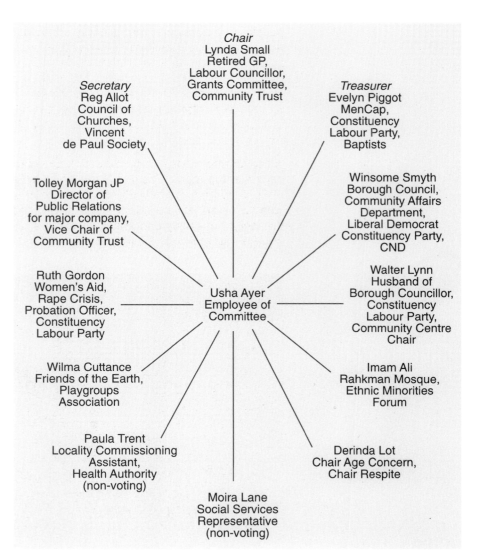

Figure 2
The management committee members of Usha's CVS and their connections with other agencies

If you were to investigate voluntary sector management committees in your local area you would probably find a great deal of overlap in membership, with the same people cropping up on different management committees, liaison committees, inter-agency working parties, and so on.

Activity 8 Magic circles

Allow about 10 minutes Look at Figure 2, which shows how the members of the management committee who direct Usha's work are linked with other local organisations. They are elected each year at a public annual general meeting. What advantages and what disadvantages do you think arise from overlapping membership of such committees in a locality?

Comment Overlapping memberships are an important way in which organisations in a locality can exchange information, and perhaps develop co-operative relationships. However, they also mean that the management of the local voluntary sector as a whole may be in the hands of a rather small group of individuals who may represent the ideas and interests of only a narrow range of local people. Concern has been expressed particularly over the possibility that people from minority ethnic backgrounds don't break into the 'magic circle' (Institute of Race Relations, 1993). This will be particularly important when the existing voluntary sector is heavily involved in locality planning. Correspondingly, many authorities, although not all (Halpin and Patel, 1993), have made special efforts to bring groups representing ethnic minorities into the planning system (Winn and Chotai, 1993; Mohammed, 1993; Jamdagni, 1996). This may be difficult, as Figure 3 indicates.

However, the more widely representative management in the voluntary sector is, the more difficult it is for organisations to keep in touch with each other, and the more difficult they find it to make common cause against the statutory authorities. And the more diverse interests are represented in the management of any one agency, the more stormy their meetings become and the more difficult it is for them to make decisions and carry them out.

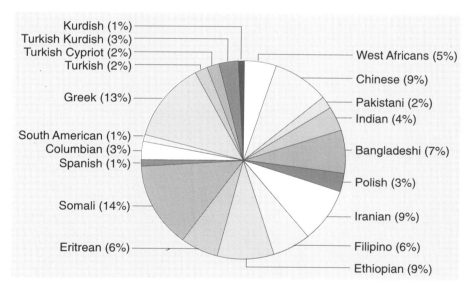

Figure 3
Consulting with minority ethnic groups is necessary, but can be expensive and time-consuming. For example, in Camden and Islington about 18 per cent of the population are from minority ethnic groups. Eighty per cent of them are from 19 groups, while the remaining 20 per cent are made up of a great many more (Jamdagni, 1996, p. 37)

3.2 Growing the mixed economy of care

Not only is Usha's post paid for from statutory sources, but the whole idea of the post came from managers in the local authority social services department who persuaded the local health authority to pay half the costs of funding it. Many 'voluntary sector' projects and organisations have been established in this way, rather than emerging unaided from 'the community'. So why should statutory authorities set up posts like this, pay for them, and place them beyond their own managerial control in voluntary agencies? The main reasons for this are closely related to the reform of health and social services brought about through the NHS and Community Care Act 1990 (and its Northern Ireland equivalent). In England, Wales and Scotland these reforms were implemented for social care in 1993; in Northern Ireland they were implemented a little earlier.

As part of the implementation of the 1990 NHS and Community Care Act, money that had been used to fund residential care was transferred from the national social security budget to local authority social services or social work departments. The social security budget is that which finances welfare benefits. In England welfare benefits are the responsibility of the Department of Social Security, not the Department of Health, which has the main responsibility for health and social care services. In the other parts of the UK there is a similar division between departments within the Welsh, Scottish and Northern Ireland Offices respectively. This transfer of money – called the Special Transitional Grant, or STG – had strings attached (Department of Health, 1994c). Only 15 per cent of it could be spent on services provided directly by the social services or the social work department itself. The remainder had to be spent on purchasing services from the independent sector. Thus, social services or social work departments had to look around for ways of spending this additional money in the independent sector. One way was to create 'voluntary sector' posts, projects and agencies on which to spend the money. Since another of their new duties was to engage in community care planning, some of these new jobs related to the locality planning process. Usha's post is one example.

Activity 9

If you can remember what you read in Unit 3, allow 5 minutes. If not, allow longer

Growing the mixed economy

From what you know already about the aims of the NHS and Community Care Act and its Northern Ireland equivalent, why do you think the government of the time earmarked some of the additional funding to local authorities for spending only on services provided by private and voluntary sector agencies?

In order to answer this you might have to turn back to Unit 3, Section 1.

Comment

One way of responding to this question would be to say that the government of the time wanted to break the monopolistic position of social services and social work departments in providing social care. The government believed that monopolies are expensive and inefficient, and that breaking them up creates competition and better quality services at keener prices. The introduction of the purchaser/provider split for social care, as in health, was designed to stimulate the development of a 'market' of alternative suppliers ('the providers'), who would compete with each other in terms of price and quality to sell their services to the purchasers. Earmarking funding for spending on private or voluntary sector provision was one way, among several, in which the government attempted to force local authorities to purchase services from outside rather than to provide them directly.

Central government made it more expensive for social services or social work departments to provide services directly themselves than to purchase from outside. But apart from residential care and, to a lesser extent, home care services (see Unit 3), there were often no independent agencies to purchase services from. So to do this they had to take some steps to bring into being independent provider agencies from which they could purchase services. One way of doing this was to hive off sections of local authority social services to an independent existence, giving them charitable status and hence putting them in the voluntary sector. Another was to stimulate the development of new voluntary sector organisations. At the time this was often called 'growing the market' or 'developing the mixed economy of care'.

Usha's job, and other jobs like it, can therefore be seen as attempts to bring into being the kinds of voluntary sector agencies from which the social services purchasers (or indeed the health authority) might purchase services, and to strengthen existing voluntary agencies so that they might be in a position to accept and manage a contract to supply a service. That is what the term 'development' means in the title of voluntary sector mental health development co-ordinator.

Key point

- The NHS and Community Care Act 1990 and its Northern Ireland equivalent forced the statutory authorities to purchase services from independent providers. But often there were no voluntary sector providers to purchase from. Some authorities responded to this by helping new voluntary sector providers to emerge.

3.3 What Usha did for the Phoenix Centre

What Usha did

This is what Usha did to help the Phoenix Centre into existence, more or less in the order in which she did it.

- First, Usha helped the group to clarify its ideas about what was wanted.

- Then she helped the group to formulate some rules for how members were going to behave towards each other.

- She wrote a constitution for the group suitable for registering it as a charity, and handled all the paperwork with the Charity Commission (this wouldn't have been necessary in Scotland) (Thompson, 1996).

- She showed members of the group how to conduct meetings so that decisions could be made, and minuted and kept to.

- Usha recruited a treasurer for the group from a retired executives scheme. In theory he was supposed to teach money management skills to members of the group, but in practice this didn't happen.

- She helped the group to apply for a small 'start-up' grant from the local community trust. Community trusts, or sometimes community foundations, are local fund-raising and grant-giving organisations that derive most of their income from company donations. In the UK the 42 community trusts dispense around £35 million a year for health and social care purposes (Association of Community Trusts and Foundations, 1997). There are other sources of local and national charitable money as well.

- Usha did library research to discover the likely extent of 'severe mental illness' among 17- to 30-year-olds. She read the report of the director of public health to find out how many people in that age group were treated in the acute psychiatric ward, and asked related questions of the managers of the local community mental health teams. She looked for articles describing user-controlled services, and contacted the members of a user-controlled service in a nearby town to arrange visits between the two groups.

- She helped the members write a fully costed business plan for a user-controlled day centre.

- She completed the necessary paperwork to make an application for funding to the National Lottery Charities Board – which failed.

- She discovered what the priorities were for health and social services development so that applications for funding could be written to meet them.

- She arranged for two members of the group to become members of a locality planning group.

- She arranged for members of the group to give a presentation about their plans to the local branches of MIND, the National Schizophrenia Fellowship, and other organisations to mobilise support, and rehearsed them in how they would give the presentation.

- She helped to write a proposal for the Phoenix project, inserted the proposal at the right time in the planning cycle, and, together with members of the group, defended it in meeting after meeting.

- Once the proposal was accepted, Usha helped the group to:
  - negotiate a contract with health and social services
  - find premises and insure them, and secure furnishings from local businesses
  - secure funding for decoration from a local pharmaceutical company
  - secure office equipment through the good offices of the community trust
  - write a user's charter, an equal opportunities policy, a policy about disruptive behaviour and one about alcohol and drug use on the premises
  - develop a job description, a contract and a disciplinary and grievance procedure for the paid centre worker, advertise the post, and interview the applicants.

Not all voluntary sector organisations, and not even all those run by service users, need to be nursed into existence by a support worker. Nor do all of them need a support worker to help them organise themselves in order to bid for finance from social services or the health authority or the National Lottery Charities Board. Many have members who are quite capable of doing this for themselves. The example was chosen to show the maximum that such a support worker might have to do. But, as you have seen, the planning and contracting process is complicated and difficult to understand, so the kind of job that Usha does can make a difference to whether or not the aspirations of some sections of the local population are recognised and acted upon. Bringing people from minority ethnic groups into the sphere of locality planning has been a particularly common kind of initiative across the UK (for example, Winn and Chotai, 1993).

The example given was of a post funded by the statutory authorities and placed in the voluntary sector. However, there is no national pattern. Sometimes jobs like Usha's are done by employees of a statutory authority, sometimes by employees of a district authority, not itself the social services authority, and sometimes the same work is done by employees of one of the large national voluntary organisations such as MIND, Mencap or Age Concern, or through voluntary sector umbrella organisations such as the Northern Ireland Voluntary Trust (McShane, 1993). Sometimes there are no support workers at all.

Key points

- Locality planning systems are complex and difficult to understand.

- Groups outside the established voluntary sector can be marginalised in locality planning systems.

- In many areas of the country posts have been created to enable the voluntary sector in general to participate in locality planning, and in particular to bring marginalised groups into the process.

Section 4
Self-advocacy

In Unit 10 you read about advocacy. Most of the comments there concerned advocating for individuals, with the advocate making a case on behalf of a would-be service user to help them get the best possible deal from services. This section, however, is about *self-advocacy*. So it is necessary to consider what the difference might be between the two practices.

4.1 Advocacy and self-advocacy

The movement towards self-advocacy has been one of the most important developments in health and social care in the 1980s and particularly in the 1990s (Robson, 1987; Crawley, 1988; Beresford and Campbell, 1990; Campbell, 1996). It has taken place across North America, New Zealand, Australia and Europe with regard to people who have physical disabilities; people with communicative difficulties, such as impaired vision or hearing; people regarded as having learning difficulties or as being mentally ill; and among older people more generally. Self-advocacy groups have taken considerable inspiration from the civil rights movements among black people, from feminism and from the gay movement. As in these movements, the major demand is to be treated as people with the same rights as other citizens, including the right to define their own needs, rather than to have them defined by others.

As you have seen from considering Usha's activities, advocacy can be practised on behalf of groups as well as on behalf of individuals. There is little difficulty in saying that Usha advocated on behalf of the Phoenix group, but what is the difference between 'advocacy' and 'self-advocacy'? In the abstract the distinction is easy enough to make. Advocates speak for people; self-advocates speak for themselves. But in practice making the distinction is more difficult. Think, for example, of the way in which Usha helped members of the group prepare a presentation for delivery to potential allies and to decision makers. In giving the presentation, were they 'speaking for themselves' or were they mouthing words that Usha had given them to say? In some ways Usha behaved like the classic advocate: the lawyer defending a client in court. Lawyers both speak on behalf of clients and coach clients in how to speak on their own behalf from the dock.

This raises the question of to whom, exactly, the plan for the Phoenix Centre belonged. Did it belong to the group, or was it a plan they were persuaded to subscribe to on the grounds that it was feasible, or acceptable or affordable, and hence more likely to be successful than some other plan they might have preferred?

In fact, for one of the real groups on which the case study was based, the 'Phoenix Centre' was very different from what they originally demanded. This group started out with one strident demand: that they as white service users should not have to be served by black staff, nor have to share facilities with black service users. In this case, the worker concerned, who was indeed an Asian woman, persuaded the group that their demands were unacceptable, and prevailed on them to modify these into a package that would have some chance of success in the competition for statutory funding. She even managed to get the group to subscribe to an equal opportunities policy for the day centre, although it is doubtful whether it will be a very comfortable place for black people to attend.

In Unit 10 Ken Simons is quoted as saying that advocates should be unconditional allies of the person they are supporting. It is obvious that for one of the groups on which the Phoenix case study was based, the worker was not an *un*conditional ally. Rather, she offered support, including advocacy, only on condition that the group changed its aims in ways acceptable to her. No doubt the racist tendencies of this group were repugnant to the worker concerned, but under other circumstances she might still have offered support only on condition that the group committed itself to a plan of action with some chance of success. Otherwise she would be wasting her time and wasting the time and effort of the group. Lawyers, likewise, are only prepared to advocate for clients when some conditions are met. For example, most lawyers will not tell lies for clients and most will draw the line at supporting a client through a course of action they think has no chance of a successful outcome.

The term 'self-advocacy' suggests that people advocate for themselves in ways that allow them to put forward their own views as they themselves see them. Perhaps this is so, but many so-called 'self-advocacy' groups rely heavily on the advice and support of paid or volunteer workers. Inevitably, this advice influences the way self-advocating people speak for themselves. Sometimes this may mean that they self-advocate for what seems possible, rather than for what they would prefer. This is not especially associated with self-advocacy in health and social care. Life often confronts people with situations where they can choose between demanding exactly what they want and getting nothing, and demanding rather less than they want and getting something. What you get depends on what other people will agree to. Deciding how far to compromise in order to be successful in the planning system is something that taxes many self-advocacy groups. The dilemma is nicely captured in the title of an article by Edna Conlan called 'Shaking hands with the devil' (1996).

All this is to say that it is very difficult to draw a line between advocacy and the kinds of self-advocacy that involve support workers or facilitators. However, two sets of ideas that are associated with self-advocacy rather than with advocacy are that practising self-advocacy helps people to develop their confidence and their self-esteem, and that self-advocacy is a process through which the people concerned learn valuable skills (The Open University, 1990b, p. 101).

In the words of Suzy Croft and Peter Beresford, who have been important figures in the English self-advocacy movement:

> *Developing our own accounts ... is the starting point for our empowerment. It means putting together our views, our versions of things. We begin by articulating our wants and experiences. Once we put our individual accounts together, we become aware of the similarities and overlaps with other people's. We discover there's nothing strange or special about us. It isn't just me. I'm not the only woman who feels lonely stuck at home with a young baby. Other people have the same problems living on income support. Our thoughts and ideas aren't just moans, grumbles and gossip. They aren't merely anecdotal or apocryphal. They don't have to be hidden, secret and illegitimate. They are helpful and important. We have the right to express them. We begin to see that they have validity alongside other more powerful accounts. We have our side of the story to tell too.*
>
> *(Croft and Beresford, 1993, p. 131)*

Croft and Beresford are commenting on the development of self-confidence and self-esteem through self-advocacy. The other important aspect is the learning of skills.

As far as possible Usha tried to assist members of the Phoenix group to do things for themselves, rather than doing things for them. She attempted to help them develop skills through *self-advocacy*.

Activity 10   Developing self-advocacy skills in the Phoenix group

Allow about 15 minutes   Look back at the list of things that Usha did with the Phoenix group. Make a list of the kinds of things she tried to help them do for themselves, and then a list of skills they might have learnt from this.

Comment   Some of the skills you might have identified include:

- **Social relationship skills** – how to get on with each other, how to make relationships with people you are negotiating with and so on, how to relate to each other in decision-making meetings.

- **Communication skills** – how to prepare and give a presentation, for example.

- **Organisational skills** – how to conduct meetings, write minutes, do forward planning, and so on. None of the group could be persuaded to learn the skills of a treasurer, but they were provided with the opportunity to learn.

Some of the things Usha did for the group are the kinds of things people often ask experts to do, rather than do themselves: for example, researching in a library, applying for charitable status, or doing financial planning.

4.2 A self-advocacy group

As long as you do not draw a very strict line between advocacy and self-advocacy it is reasonable to say that the Phoenix group was one kind of self-advocacy group. In Activity 11 you will be asked to listen to an

A meeting of the Leavesden self-advocacy group

audio cassette about the development of another self-advocacy group, this time in the field of learning disabilities. The cassette you will hear features the self-advocacy group at Leavesden Hospital in Hertfordshire. This was a large 'mental handicap' hospital like Lennox Castle (Unit 16). The formation of the group more or less coincided with plans to close the hospital and disperse its inmates into the community. Thinking about how inmates were going to accommodate themselves to life outside may have encouraged staff and management to take the idea of self-advocacy seriously. The cassette was made in 1990, three or four years after the self-advocacy group was established, and at a time when self-advocacy groups were still rather controversial. The members of the Leavesden group now live in the community but many are still members of self-advocacy groups linked into the national People First network. You saw some work that has come from this organisation in Section 1.

Activity 11 **Self-advocacy at Leavesden**

Allow about 25 minutes

Find Audio Cassette 5, side 1, which is about the Leavesden self-advocacy group. Two members of the group, Ronnie Palmer and Ronnie Lewis, and its facilitator (Dave Lewis) tell you about the development of the group, and what it had done in the way of organising events and influencing services. All of these are important matters. But you have already considered something similar in relation to the Phoenix group. So for this activity pay particular attention to what the cassette tells you about the way the self-advocacy group provided opportunities for its members to develop their skills and their self-esteem. Jot down your own notes about this as you listen to the recording.

Comment

Here is what Fiona Williams said about the recording in another OU course:

> People gain a lot from their membership of the group, as two of the tape contributors indicate: 'it's made my life completely good really'. 'I get out more things about how I feel'. Other attractions of the group at a personal level include opportunities to:
> * attend a self-advocacy conference
> * take part in leisure and sports activities such as drama, football, hockey and running
> * enjoy parties and pub lunches
> * get help with personal problems
> * develop more two-way relationships and friendships with staff.
>
> (The Open University, 1990a, p. 20)

The late Anita Binns, a leading member of the self-advocacy movement among people with learning difficulties

The recording gave you a glimpse of the way the Leavesden group facilitated self-development, at least with regard to the two leading members of the group who spoke on the tape. Think back to the discussion on providing information to help people access services in Section 1. Self-advocacy gives people the confidence and the support to take advantage of services in a way that simply providing information does not. The next activity is designed to give you a better picture of the importance of self-advocacy in terms of someone's biography. It features Anita Binns, another graduate of the self-advocacy movement, but this time in Nottingham and later Gateshead.

Activity 12   Anita's story

Allow about 15 minutes

Turn to the Offprints Book and find Offprint 25 'Anita's story', which is derived from an interview with the late Anita Binns. When you read it you will see that the story falls into a 'before' and 'after' pattern. As you read it, try jotting down what Anita could do after she developed the skills of self-advocacy, which she didn't seem able to do before. The reference to 'Skills' in the offprint is a reference to the 'Skills for self-advocacy programme': a training programme for self-advocacy.

Comment

Here are some of the befores and afters you might have noted:

Before	After
Couldn't stand up for herself without having a blazing row	Could firmly and calmly put a social worker in his place
Allowed herself to be stigmatised and put upon, treated as an inferior and given the least desirable tasks to do	Wouldn't allow this to happen again
Didn't know how to advocate for herself	Knows very well how to advocate for herself
Couldn't have helped others to self-advocate	Regularly helps others develop these skills
Didn't have any idea of her rights, or of the responsibilities which might go with these	Can assert her rights and can address a conference on this topic
Couldn't have addressed a conference	Is a seasoned conference performer
(Probably) couldn't have told her life story in such a lucid way	Is able to tell her life story as a story of personal success, and as the success of a movement
Didn't have a very interesting life story to tell	Now has a very interesting life story to tell and lots of opportunities to tell it – at conferences, in the publications of People First and The Open University, and in other publications

A quicker way of saying all this would be to say that through self-advocacy Anita has transformed herself into a person likely to engage the interests of others and able to make a valuable contribution to *their* lives.

Key points

- The movement for self-advocacy has been one of the most important developments in health and social care in the 1980s and 1990s.

- Self-advocacy means speaking for yourself, rather than having someone speak on your behalf. It usually implies doing so with the support of a self-advocacy group.

- It is often difficult to distinguish self-advocacy from advocacy when support workers or facilitators are employed to assist self-advocacy groups.

- Two things claimed for self-advocacy but not for advocacy are that practising self-advocacy helps people gain confidence and self-esteem, and develop valuable skills.

This section has been about self-advocacy groups and self-advocacy skills. It ended by considering the importance of these for self-development. The next section is again about self-advocacy, but returns to the topic of how self-advocacy can give service users a voice in the way services are planned, managed and provided.

Study skills: Ways of reporting (Part 1)

Whether as a carer, or as a student of care, you need to become skilled both at reading and writing reports of care situations. A report is never simply 'the facts' of the situation. Any report has to select from many potentially relevant facts. Moreover, the way the report is written (or spoken) inevitably gives a particular 'slant' to the story. It makes a lot of difference who is reporting to whom, and what they are trying to report about and why.

You can easily see this by looking back at Anita Binns's story. Take just the first four paragraphs of Offprint 25; they outline an incident involving Anita at an Adult Training Centre (ATC). This is an oral report of the incident by Anita herself, recorded on audio tape in an interview.

Activity 13   **Ways of reporting**

Allow about 30 minutes

Read the first four paragraphs of Offprint 25 again and make notes of what you think happened. Then write a few lines presenting a 'report' of the incident.

After that read the five reports below.

1   It was decided that the most appropriate option for Ms Binns was sheltered accommodation with opportunities for employment. However, with arrangements already well advanced she refused point blank to consider them. After an emotional outburst she severed her links with the Centre.

2   The meeting was badly handled. The client had not been prepared in advance for a relocation. Despite best efforts to provide emotional support, management's unsympathetic, heavy-handed approach led to a complete breakdown of relations.

3   Anita Binns is a challenging client, prone to sharp, unpredictable mood swings. She is suspicious of strange people and situations and finds it difficult to cope with change. She is resistant to efforts to help her and quickly becomes confrontational.

4   Although she lacks self-confidence and is easily overcome by her feelings, Anita is a shrewd judge of people and situations. She quickly recognised that Centre management, for their own convenience, intended to dispatch her to alternative provision without due consultation or respect for her wishes and rights. She put up a stout resistance and was not cowed by threats of suspension.

5   A. Binns. Difficult client. Refused appropriate provision. Became confrontational. Temporary suspension from the Centre.

These reports were made up using only the information in Anita's account. Is your report at all like any of these? If not, why do you think yours is different? Does it have a different slant? If so, what is your slant?

Look back at these five reports and at your own. For each try to answer these questions.

*   *Who* would write a report of this kind?
*   *To whom* would it be written?
*   *What* is it a report about?
*   *Why* would a report of this kind be written? What is its *purpose*?

Comment   These made-up reports were written to show how differently the same events could be reported.

1   This kind of report might perhaps be written by a worker at the ATC, as case notes on Anita which might be read by other agencies. The report focuses on the efforts made by the ATC to meet Anita's needs and her unco-operative response. Its purpose is to demonstrate that the ATC did a reasonable job of discharging its duties towards Anita.

2   This type of report would certainly not be written by the ATC management. More likely, it would be written by Anita's social worker, to be read by social work colleagues. The report is about the failure of the ATC management to handle communications with Anita sensitively. Although in her own account Anita suggests that it was the social worker who should have told her about the move, there is no mention of this, only of the emotional support the social worker offered. The purpose seems to be to criticise the regime at the ATC.

3   This kind of report might perhaps be written by someone at the ATC with responsibility for assessing Anita, to be read by colleagues who have dealings with her. Its focus is on Anita herself rather than the incident. It reads motives and personal characteristics into her actions and slots her into psychological categories. The message is that Anita's problems lie within herself, rather than in difficult circumstances or the way she has been treated.

4   This is a more sympathetic account by someone with responsibility for assessing Anita. Perhaps it is to be read by colleagues at a case conference. Instead of focusing on inner weaknesses, it is about her strengths. It criticises ATC management and commends Anita's resourcefulness and resilience.

5   This might be a routine record made by a member of ATC staff, to be read only if queries about Anita's case should arise later. Like the first report it emphasises that the ATC discharged its duties properly and that the problems arose from Anita's side.

Notice that just changing small things alters the way the reports read. For example, how Anita is referred to: Ms Binns, the client, Anita Binns, Anita, A. Binns. Each style positions the report writer differently in relation to Anita. Were you able to work out who you were reporting as and to whom, and what the purpose of your report was?

The other account to mention is Anita's own. She is reporting as one person in conversation with another, trying to draw on the listener's sympathy. Her account emphasises the people involved in the situation and their relationship to her. She focuses on the unfairness and insensitivity of others and her own emotional reactions, but also her resilience. It is actually quite hard to get to grips with what happened at the ATC. Anita has not provided some of the basics that a report requires. She does not establish the *general context* and the *specific circumstances*. Nor is it very clear *where her account is leading*, or what its *purpose* is. This is understandable, since she has difficulties expressing herself and wasn't setting out to give a 'report' anyway. But you get a useful insight into why a report needs to indicate context and purpose. Although the other reports above do not spell out context and purpose explicitly, they signal them in subtle ways, as you have seen.

Study skills: Ways of reporting (Part 2)

Clearly, the same incident can give rise to very different accounts. It makes a lot of difference who is reporting to whom and why. As a reader, you need to develop a sensitivity to what lies behind the reports you read. The words on the page are only part of the story. Becoming a skilled reader means being able to read 'critically', weighing up the quality of the case that is being made at the same time as taking in its details.

Section 5
Opportunities for self-advocates

In Section 4 you saw how self-advocacy influenced the way services were provided at Leavesden, and in Section 3 how, for the Phoenix project, it featured in the locality planning process. The example of the work of People First in Section 1 shows how self-advocacy can lead to better information being provided to service users. The following activity attempts to draw these threads together and to look at the whole range of possibilities for self-advocacy in health and social care.

Activity 14 Identifying opportunities

Allow about 20 minutes For this activity you will need to look again at Figure 1 (p. 26). Trace your way round the diagram and for each numbered stage of the planning process – *except stage 4* – jot down some ways in which the views of service users *might* be made to enter into the process. This might be through self-advocacy or through some other means, such as a researcher using a questionnaire to ask their opinions. If you are familiar with the services in your own area, try to identify the stages at which service users are actually involved and the opportunities that are missed.

Comment Here are some possibilities. Your points may not marry up with the numbered stages in the same way as given below. Don't worry about that. Dividing a continuous process into stages is bound to be rather arbitrary. You might have thought of more possibilities. You might like to add the list below to your own.

Stage	Opportunities for involvement
1 Assessment of community need	Service users might be consulted passively, through research or at consultation meetings, or they might articulate their needs more forcefully, through self-advocacy.
2 Audit of provision	Service users might do their own audit. Or research might be conducted to see what services people actually use and how far they think these serve their needs.
3 Planning, prioritising, budgeting	Giving groups of service users an important role in the locality planning system. Surveys of service users could determine what *their* priorities are. Self-advocacy could force their own priorities up the planning agenda.
5 Implementing the plan	Groups of service users could be used as expert consultants to draw up the specifications for contracts. Or the specifications for contracts could be derived from survey research using interviews or questionnaires. As in the case of the Phoenix Centre, service users might take a major role in running their own services.
6 Monitoring implementation	Service users might be involved in deciding what information is used for monitoring (as in stage 5). Contracts might specify that providers survey user satisfaction as a way of monitoring the quality of the service.
7 Evaluation of provision	Service users' views must always be sought in evaluating the quality of services. Service users might conduct evaluation research on their own behalf (Whittaker *et al.*, 1990; Nettle, 1996).

Activity 14 concentrated on planning services for whole categories of people. But these services will be used for individuals. Much the same comments apply to opportunities for involving a client in the *individual* care planning process: from assessment, through care planning, to delivering a service, monitoring how things are going, and evaluating it at a review. *Care Management and Assessment: Practitioners' Guide* (Department of Health Social Services Inspectorate/Scottish Social Work Group, 1991), one of the official manuals for implementing the 1990 NHS and Community Care Act in England, Wales and Scotland, and *Care Management* (Northern Ireland Office, 1991), the equivalent for Northern Ireland, both encourage practitioners to assist service users in defining their own needs, and both allow for advocates to be present at the assessment or review if the service user so desires. Unit 10 (Section 4.1) referred to the study by Baldock and Ungerson (1994) that showed how some service users and informal carers are involved in 'packaging' the care for themselves by choosing from what is available and purchasing some of it on a private basis. Unit 3 also dealt with making direct payments to service users, which allows them to purchase services and employ staff directly as personal assistants. You read the arguments in favour of this by Jenny Morris in her Reader chapter. Regular reviews of care are regarded as good practice in the official guidance, and for mental health work are almost mandatory (Department of Health, 1995). Such reviews should record the service user's satisfaction or otherwise. They offer another routine opportunity for canvassing the views of service users about what is provided at the individual level. Looking at all the records of reviews would also provide a picture of the preferences and dissatisfactions of large numbers of service users.

Key point

- Involving service users need not be restricted to giving them questionnaires or mounting events called 'consultations'. Opportunities for involvement occur throughout the process of planning, managing, delivering, monitoring and evaluating services. At the individual level they occur throughout the process of assessing, care planning, care delivery and review.

Perhaps the most important message of Activity 14 is that involving service users should not be something that just occurs at events called 'consultations' but something that should permeate the system as a whole. Space prevents a detailed treatment of all the ways in which service user involvement might be enhanced, so the text that follows deals with contracts and contracting (stage 5 on Figure 1) and attempts to draw some general points from this.

5.1 Contracts, standards and consultation

Contracts between purchaser and provider became an important feature of health and social care during the 1990s. You considered the contracts between a local authority social services department and a private home care agency (Independent Nursing Services) in Unit 3. Contracts themselves are not new in health and social care. Private medical care has always involved contracts, usually between a medical insurance company (the purchaser) and a provider of medical services. Since the inception of the NHS, GPs, dentists and ophthalmic opticians have had contracts with the NHS, specifying the services they should supply and the remuneration they should receive for this. For a very long time social services departments have been issuing contracts to private and voluntary children's homes. What is new is that in the mixed economy of care (Unit 3, Section 4.1) many more services are contracted out by statutory authorities – hence there are many more contracts. Contracts have become the major means through which agreements between agencies are negotiated and recorded, and everyone now pays more attention to making sure that contracts clearly specify what is required by the purchaser and what income will accrue to the provider.

Many purchasers have tried to use contracting to drive up the quality of provision. In Unit 3 you heard that this was something welcomed by the manager of Independent Nursing Services, as a way of driving 'cowboy' operators out of business. So, for example, it is common for health authorities and social services or social work departments to require a contractor to be adequately insured, to have accessible complaints procedures, to make and implement training plans and to have policies for equal opportunities, health and safety, confidentiality, and so on. You will probably remember some of these from the Phoenix Centre case study. These are all areas where voluntary and private sector agencies were often very weak before the arrival of the 'contract culture' (Knight, 1993). Some purchasers also use an annual review of the contract as a way of setting targets for better performance in the coming year.

Similarly, in order for the purchaser to judge whether the contract is being complied with, and whether such contracts are worth making, it is usual to require the provider to supply information at regular intervals. These so-called 'monitoring data' might be about numbers of people using a service, their satisfaction with it, the training undertaken by staff and, of course, evidence that the money paid was spent for the purposes intended. When the service concerned is subject to inspection, as in the case of residential care (see Unit 8, Section 5), then independent inspection reports provide another source of evidence for the purchaser.

A further area in which purchasers often use their financial power over providers is in requiring providers to consult more with those who use their services and to involve them more fully in the management of the agency. Rather more rarely, purchasers themselves involve service users in setting the terms of the contracts. For example, in Newcastle, the Mental Health Consumer Group, which is made up of people who use mental health services, provides representatives for the working parties of the health authority that drafts contracts with the providers of mental health services, particularly with the NHS Mental Health Trust (Barker *et al.*, 1993). Health authorities elsewhere have either involved black service users in drawing up contract specifications, or have submitted draft specifications to black user groups for their comments (Mohammed, 1993; Jamdagni, 1996).

It is worth considering what thought goes into drafting contracts and what contractor and contractee might negotiate about, apart from the price. Contracting can be quite complicated, so the following activity features a rather simple service: meals on wheels.

Activity 15   **Contracting for quality**

Allow about 15 minutes   For this activity put yourself in the position of a local authority that is about to issue a contract to the local Women's Royal Voluntary Service (WRVS) to provide a meals-on-wheels service. Write down one or two standards that the WRVS should be required to meet to ensure that the service will be of an acceptable quality. You might choose something to do with frequency of delivery, punctuality of delivery, range of choice, palatability of food, nutritional quality of food, demeanour of delivery drivers. You can see how contracts often get to be quite long documents. For this activity, however, you should choose only one or two required standards. When you have chosen, write down how the WRVS might provide information – monitoring data – to show it had met the standards required.

Comment   Some of the possible standards are more difficult to specify than others. It is relatively easy to specify that meals should be delivered on so many days a week, or perhaps that on 90 per cent of occasions meals should be delivered within plus or minus 30 minutes of the time agreed with the recipient. It is much more difficult to specify what 'palatability' means, or what is an 'acceptable range of choice'. These are matters that depend very much on the personal tastes of the people receiving the meals. For example, 'always offering halal meat' (for Muslims) is not the same as 'always offering halal meat cooked in an appetising way' (Jamdagni, 1994). Specifying 'always offering a choice of three main courses' may not be acceptable to someone who dislikes all three! There is a similar range of ease and difficulty about monitoring data. For delivery on time, a synopsis of drivers' time sheets might be quite adequate, but for judging whether the meals were indeed sufficiently palatable, or whether an acceptable range of choices had been offered, the WRVS would need to find a way of canvassing the opinions of service users. This is even more necessary for services where what is 'delivered' is less tangible than a meal – counselling for example.

You will probably realise that this activity really put the cart before the horse, or the wheels before the meals. Better practice would be to involve the users of the service from the outset in determining what the standards should be, and involve them thereafter in giving their opinion on whether the standards had been met. There is still the question, however, of how they might be involved.

5.2 Consultation, involvement and research

Offprint 26 'Sandwell – mental health' gives an account of how some draft specifications for an advocacy service for black patients were drawn up following research with black service users. Note that this is an advocacy, not a self-advocacy, service, although most advocacy services of this kind try to support clients in speaking for themselves rather than simply speaking for them. The Sandwell specifications don't go as far as you went in Activity 15 in specifying standards closely or identifying the evidence that might be used to decide whether standards had been met. But they are a step on the way to this.

Activity 16   **Contract specifications from research**

Allow about 15 minutes

Read Offprint 26 for what it tells you about these black service users' views on mental health services. When you have read it think about the differences between deriving the specifications for a service in this way, through research, and deriving them through a process of supported self-advocacy, as they were in Usha's work with the Phoenix group. What do you think are the advantages and disadvantages of each method?

Comment

Involving service users through self-advocacy, as in the Phoenix project

Advantages

Through the process of self-advocacy, people learn skills they wouldn't otherwise learn, gain confidence and may be placed in a better position to use the services available to satisfy their needs.

Self-advocacy groups can act together to pressurise services to respond to their views. Their activities can lead to successes, which help members to value themselves.

Disadvantages

Self-advocacy groups may work to suppress the views of minorities within the group, so that the views articulated are not representative of all. Sometimes such groups become the creature of a charismatic group facilitator, and not really *self-advocacy* groups at all (George, 1995). Sometimes such groups may colonise a particular service, making it unattractive to others.

Involving service users through research, as in Sandwell

A research approach may allow opinions to be expressed free from the pressure of a group or a professional facilitator. It protects the views of minorities within the group from being silenced by the others. Views can be recorded systematically and accurately, and separately for individuals. If all service users (or a representative sample of service users) are asked, the research has a good chance of reflecting the diversity of opinions.

Contrary to the above, it is sometimes argued that people are over-awed by researchers and are empowered to express their true opinions only when supported by other like-minded individuals.

Those consulted as research subjects learn and gain little from the process itself – although they might gain from their opinions being used to design services to meet their needs.

In thinking of your answer you might have recalled the Leavesden recording and have wondered whether the experience of the two main contributors was characteristic of the group as a whole. They were both male and highly articulate, while some members of the group were female and/or less articulate. The problem of less assertive minorities being overwhelmed in groups is recognised by leading figures in the self-advocacy movement, but not necessarily by all the members of all the groups (Croft and Beresford, 1993). You may also have wondered how far this group, started and presided over by hospital staff, was inhibited by them (The Open University, 1990a). On the other hand, there is no doubt that being a member of a self-advocacy group can be a positive learning experience, while being asked questions by a researcher might not be. The Sandwell offprint noted that interviews had to be arranged to avoid interviewees being 'overwhelmed and fatigued by the list of questions'.

There are also some practical issues to consider in deciding which method of involving service users in setting and monitoring standards is more appropriate. These can be represented by thinking about service user groups, or constituencies, in terms of a number of dimensions, as in Figure 4.

The constituency of service users:	
is large in number	is small in number
is heterogeneous	is homogeneous
has fleeting contacts with services	has long-term contacts with services
has members who don't get to know each other in using services	has members who do get to know each other in using services

Figure 4
Some dimensions of service user constituencies

Both examples of self-advocacy featured in this unit (the Phoenix and Leavesden groups) would be mapped on the right-hand side for each dimension in Figure 4, although perhaps too many assumptions should not be made about their being homogeneous groups. Groups are made up of individuals, after all. The circumstances of both groups made them ideal for the development of self-advocacy. By contrast, people using many other kinds of services would be mapped further towards the left-hand side for each dimension – for example the group of people who featured in the research in Sandwell. The meals-on-wheels service you considered is an even better example of mapping towards the left. The customers are numerous. Their contacts with the service are usually limited to five minutes at each delivery. Most of them don't know each other and although some may be long-term users, others will not be. The opportunities for a self-advocacy approach are obviously limited. So, to complete Activity 15, probably the best way of canvassing users' views in setting standards and monitoring whether they had been met would be to use some kind of research technique, such as questionnaires or interviews. Something to note in passing is that communication difficulties do not rule out either self-advocacy or consultation through other means. For example, Au and Skipp (1994) report on the success of consulting people with profound learning difficulties, sometimes without the power of speech, in order to draw up contract specifications for day care in Westminster. Telephone conferencing has been used to overcome the problem of consulting housebound people (Tozer, 1995) and to give them an opportunity to quiz health and social services managers (Gomm, 1996).

Key points

- Self-advocacy is one way in which service users can be involved in the planning and management of services. It can increase self-confidence and develop valuable skills.

- But self-advocacy requires special conditions. It is usually more feasible where the user group is small and relatively homogeneous, and where use of services is long term and brings service users into contact with each other.

- There is always a danger that relatively small groups of service users will colonise key positions, crowding out other, less articulate, users or would-be users with different views.

- Research can be a more reliable way of gaining information about the experiences and preferences of *all* service users and potential service users.

- But research involves users only in a passive way, as providers of answers to researchers' questions. They learn little from the process unless they take the role of researcher.

Telephone conferencing can be used to allow housebound people to participate in community care planning – these telephone conference participants meet face to face for the first time

This section helped you review the many points in the planning, delivery and evaluation process at which service users might be involved to a greater degree than being passive recipients or passive providers of information. The section could not deal with all the possible opportunities, so it focused on contracting, setting standards for contracts and monitoring that standards have been met, and how service users might be involved in this. Similar comments might have been made about the other opportunities reviewed. The section also looked at two ways of involving service users: through a process of self-advocacy and through research. It looked at the strengths and weaknesses of both, and at some practical matters which sometimes make the one, and sometimes the other, approach more appropriate.

Conclusion

There were four core questions for this unit. Now is the time to review how they were addressed.

The first question was:

- Why is it often so difficult to find out about the services available in a local area, and what measures can be taken to improve the quality and dissemination of information about services?

The main reasons for the difficulties lie in the nature of the system itself. No one would sit down and design a health and social care system like this one from scratch. It has developed historically through a process which reforms a bit here, cuts a bit out there and bolts another piece on elsewhere. Moreover, the reforms of the early 1990s have encouraged diversity of provision, and particularly the development of more independent providers. The result is a system that is difficult to know about and can be awkward to access. But, equally, no one looks forward to the trauma of a root and branch reform. Practical measures to improve the quality of information include obvious ones, such as making it more widely available and easier to understand. But there are limits on how much simply providing information can achieve, because many people need support to use the information they are given.

New technology might help in disseminating comprehensive, up-to-date and accessible information to practitioners and to other people who advise potential users of services.

The second question was:

- How do the diverse health and social care services in an area attempt to co-ordinate their activities through locality planning?

Section 2 made an attempt to describe locality planning – but remember that this is done differently in different areas of the country. Given the complexity of what is to be planned and the many groups involved, it always looks messy from the outside, and it is a rather haphazard process anyway. Attention was drawn to the importance of various kinds of information used in locality planning and to the political nature of the process, given that groups with competing interests are involved.

The third question was:

- How can service users be more fully involved in the planning, management and evaluation of the services they use?

Perhaps the most important point made in this connection was that there are opportunities throughout the health and social care process to involve service users more fully. These were reviewed in Section 5. The unit paid most attention to involving organised groups of service users:

1   in locality planning and in the delivery of a user-led service, through the fictional example of the Phoenix Centre (Sections 2 and 3)

2   in the organisation of life in a long-stay hospital, through the example of the Leavesden self-advocacy group (Section 4)

3   and in specifying the terms for contracts between purchasers and providers (Section 5).

With regard to locality planning you will have seen that organised groups of service users, and indeed many other kinds of independent group, may need considerable support from workers such as Usha Ayer if they are to be fully involved in the process. Only in some areas of the country is such support funded by statutory agencies, and then usually only for some care groups and not for others. In other circumstances support might come from national organisations working locally, for example, Age Concern, or MIND, or the Carers National Association; or from local umbrella organisations such as CVSs or community councils (or, in Northern Ireland, the Northern Ireland Voluntary Trust); or from local community health councils (in Scotland, local health councils; in Northern Ireland, health and social service councils). Some groups may find no support at all.

The unit also suggested two main ways in which service user involvement might be facilitated. One was through developing self-advocacy, which offers service users active roles in the system and may make a considerable contribution to their personal development (Section 4). This relates to the fourth core question:

• What skills and what support do service users need in order to be more fully involved?

Most of the skills were identified through Activities 10, 11 and 12.

The other suggested way of involving service users is by using various kinds of research techniques, or through 'passive' consultation, where users of services merely supply information. Practical considerations often determine whether self-advocacy or research is more appropriate. Only some kinds of health and care circumstances lend themselves well to the development of self-advocacy groups, although where services are delivered on an *individual* basis there are usually opportunities to help clients to be more self-advocating, and to do more for themselves.

References

Association of Community Trusts and Foundations (1997) *Newsletter of UK Community Trusts and Foundations*, May.

Atkinson, D. and Williams, F. (eds) (1990) *Know Me as I Am: An Anthology of Prose, Poetry and Art by People with Learning Difficulties*, Hodder & Stoughton, London.

Audit Commission (1994) *Finding a Place: A Review of Adult Mental Health Services*, HMSO, London.

Au, S. and Skipp, P. (1994) 'Loud and clear', *Care Weekly*, 23 June, pp. 14–15.

Audit Commission (1995) *For Your Information: A Study of Information Management and Systems in the Acute Hospital*, HMSO, London.

Baldock, J. and Ungerson, C. (1994) *Becoming Conscious of Community Care: Households in the Mixed Economy of Care*, Joseph Rowntree Foundation, York.

Barker, I., Maines, K. and Wright, L. (1993) 'Consumers' voices in purchasing' in Beresford, P. and Harding, T. (eds) *A Challenge to Change: Practical Experiences of Building User-Led Services*, National Institute for Social Work, London.

Beresford, P. and Campbell, P. (1990) 'Disabled people, service users, user involvement and representation', *Disability and Society*, Vol. 9, No. 3, pp. 315–25.

Bowling, A. (1993) *What People Say About Prioritising Health Services*, King's Fund, London.

Brighton Polytechnic (1992) *The Evaluation of the Whitehawk Project*, report presented to the Brighton Health Authority and TEED, Brighton Polytechnic, Brighton.

Brindle, D. (1995) 'The consultation cure', *Guardian*, 10 May, p. 10.

Bromley Health (1995) *Local NHS Care Purchasing and Prioritising from the Perspective of Bromley Residents*, Bromley Health, Hayes.

Campbell, P. (1996) 'The history of the user movement in the United Kingdom' in Heller, T., Reynolds, J., Gomm, R., Muston, R. and Pattison, S. (eds) *Mental Health Matters: A Reader*, Macmillan, Basingstoke.

Crawley, B. (1988) *The Growing Voice: A Survey of Self-Advocacy Groups in ATCs and Hospitals: Great Britain*, CMH Publications, London.

Conlan, E. (1996) 'Shaking hands with the devil' in Read, J. and Reynolds, J. (eds) *Speaking Our Minds: An Anthology*, Macmillan, Basingstoke.

Croft, S. and Beresford, P. (1993) *Getting Involved: A Practical Manual*, Joseph Rowntree Foundation, York.

Cross, M. (1997a) 'Getting hooked', *Health Services Journal*, 27 February, p. 16.

Cross, M. (1997b) 'Executive shelves plans for NHS web', *Health Services Journal*, 10 April, p. 4.

Cutts, M. and Maher, C. (1980) *Writing Plain English*, Plain English Campaign, London.

Davies, J. and Kelly, M. (eds) (1993) *Healthy Cities: Research and Practice*, Routledge, London.

Department of Health (1990) *Joint Health and Social Services Circular: The Care Programme Approach for People with a Mental Illness Referred to Psychiatric Services*, DoH (1990) HC(90) LASS(90) 11, Department of Health, London.

Department of Health (1994a) *Healthy Alliances*, HMSO, London.

Department of Health (1994b) *People with a Mental Illness: Local Authority Specific Grant for 1994/5*, Department of Health, London.

Department of Health (1994c) *Community Care Special Transitional Grant – Form STG2*, Department of Health, London.

Department of Health (1995) *Building Bridges: A Guide to Arrangements for Inter-Agency Working for the Care and Protection of Severely Mentally Ill People*, HMSO, London.

Department of Health (1996) *Review of Purchasing of Mental Health Services by Health Authorities in England*, Department of Health, London.

Department of Health/Department of the Environment (1995) *Building Partnerships for Success: Community Care Development Programmes*, Department of Health, London.

Department of Health Social Services Inspectorate/Scottish Social Work Group (1991) *Care Management and Assessment: Practitioners' Guide*, HMSO, London.

George, M. (1995) 'Rules of engagement', *Community Care*, 7–13 September, pp. 16–17.

Gomm, M. (1996) *Report on Pilot Project, 'Three Way Calling for Housebound Older People'*, Stevenage Voluntary Forum for Services for Older People, Stevenage.

Gottlieb, B. (ed.) (1981) *Social Networks and Social Support*, Sage, London.

Halpin, E. and Patel, V. (1993) *Community Care Project: A Summary Report*, Northern Health, Social Services and Social Security Forum, Bradford.

Health Promotion Wales/Hybu lechyd Cymru (1994) *Helping Communities to Better Health: The Community Development Approach*, Health Promotion Wales/Hybu lechyd Cymru, Cardiff.

Hudson, B. (1997) 'The youth of today', *Health Services Journal*, 2 January, pp. 24–5.

Institute of Race Relations (1993) *Community Care: The Black Experience*, Institute of Race Relations, London.

Jamdagni, L. (1994) 'The tale of the chapatti maker', *King's Fund News*, Winter, p. 17.

Jamdagni, L. (1996) *Purchasing for Black Populations*, King's Fund, London.

Joint Advisory Group for Older People (1995) *Directory for the Over 60s in Milton Keynes 1995–6*, Joint Advisory Group for Older People, Milton Keynes.

Knight, B. (1993) *Voluntary Action* (the Centris Report), HMSO, London.

Lazarsfeld, P., Berelson, B. and Gaudet, H. (1944) *The People's Choice*, Columbia University Press, New York.

Lindow, V. (1994) *Self-Help Alternatives in Mental Health Services*, MIND, London.

MacIntosh, M. (1987) 'Effective media for voluntary sector promotion', *Communicate!*, No. 27, pp. 5–6.

McShane, L. (1993) *Community Support: A Pilot Programme*, Northern Ireland Voluntary Trust, Belfast.

Meltzer, H., Gill, B., Petticrew, M. and Hinds, K. (1995) *The Prevalence of Psychiatric Morbidity Among Adults Living in Private Households*, OPCS Surveys of Psychiatric Morbidity in Great Britain, Office of Population Censuses and Surveys, HMSO, London.

Moffatt, V. (1993) *Keep It Simple: A Guide to Creating Accessible Documents for People with Learning Difficulties*, Southwark Information, London Borough of Southwark.

Mohammed, S. (1993) *User-Sensitive Purchasing*, King's Fund, London.

National Association of Health Authorities and Trusts (1993) *Listening to Local Voices*, National Association of Health Authorities and Trusts, Birmingham.

National Association of Health Authorities and Trusts (1996) *The NHS Handbook*, JMH Publishing, Tunbridge Wells.

National Health Service Management Executive (1992) *Local Voices: The Views of People in Purchasing for Health*, NHSME, London.

National Health Service Management Executive (1995) *Priorities and Planning Guidance for the NHS*, NHSME, London.

Nettle, M. (1996) 'Listening in the asylum' in Read, J. and Reynolds, J. (eds) *Speaking Our Minds*, Macmillan, Basingstoke.

Northern Ireland Office (1991) *Care Management: Guidance on Assessment and the Provision of Community Care*, HMSO, Belfast.

Ogden, J. (1996) 'Open court', *Health Services Journal*, 9 May, p. 12.

The Open University (1990a) K668 *Mental Handicap: Changing Perspectives*, Media Notes, The Open University, Milton Keynes.

The Open University (1990b) K668 *Mental Handicap: Changing Perspectives*, Workbook 3, *Transitions and Change*, The Open University, Milton Keynes.

People First (1993) *Oi! It's My Assessment*, People First, London.

People First (1994) *Making Information and Words Easier to Understand*, People First, London.

Pierson, J. (1996) 'Hitch a ride', *Community Care*, 11–17 April, pp. 24–5.

Robson, G. (1987) 'Nagging: models of advocacy' in Barker, I. and Peck, E. (eds) *Power in Strange Places: User Empowerment in Mental Health Services*, Good Practices in Mental Health, London.

Silicon Bridge Research (1997) *Healthcare IT Market Profile*, Silicon Bridge Research, London.

Smith, J. and Shapiro, J. (1997) 'Local call', *Health Services Journal*, 9 January, pp. 26–7.

Sutton, P. (1995) 'Built for the future', *Community Care*, 7–13 December, pp. 16–17.

Tackling Drugs Together (White Paper) (1995), HMSO, London.

Thompson, A. (1996) 'Charitable trust', *Community Care*, 25–31 January, pp. 16–17.

Tozer, R. (1995) *Older People Having a Say in Community Care*, York Publishing Services for Social Policy Research Unit, University of York.

University of Warwick (1993) *Caring is Jargon Free*, Social Care Centre for Practice and Staff Development, University of Warwick, Coventry.

Valios, N. (1996) 'Purchasing pilots start in province', *Community Care*, 28 March–3 April, p. 8.

Whitehead, M. (1989) *Swimming Upstream: Trends and Prospects in Education for Health*, Research Report No. 5, King's Fund, London.

Whittaker, A., Gardner, S. and Kershaw, J. (1990) *Services Evaluation by People with Learning Difficulties*, King's Fund, London.

Wiltshire Social Services (1993) *The Friendly Guide to Care in the Community for People with Learning Difficulties*, Wiltshire Social Services, Salisbury.

Winn, L. and Chotai, N. (1993) 'Community development: working with black and ethnic minority groups' in Winn, L. (ed.) *Power to the People: The Key to Responsive Services in Health and Social Care*, King's Fund, London.

Acknowledgements

Grateful acknowledgement is made to the following sources for permission to reproduce material in this unit:

Text

pp. 16–17: Directory for the Over 60s in Milton Keynes 1995–6, Age Concern Milton Keynes.

Illustrations

p. 10: Courtesy of the Partially Sighted Society; *p. 11: Oi! It's My Assessment*, People First; *p. 18 (top)*: Courtesy of Herts TEC/Photo: John Shorthouse; *p. 18 (bottom)*: Courtesy of Community Information Directorate, Hertfordshire County Council; *Figure 3*: Jamdagni, L. (1996) *Purchasing for Black Populations*, King's Fund; *p. 45*: Estate of the late Anita Binns; *p. 55*: Courtesy of Herts and Essex Newspapers Ltd.

Unit 19

Records and Confidentiality

Prepared for the course team by Roger Gomm

While you are working on Unit 19, you will need:
- Offprints Book
- Wallchart

Contents

Introduction

Confidentiality is one of the important values stressed by all the professional bodies concerned with health and social care, and in all the major syllabuses for training health and social care practitioners. The knowledge you gain about confidentiality in this unit will be put to use in Unit 21, which asks you to consider how a confidentiality policy might be applied in practice.

One reason why recording is an important topic is that so much effort in health and social care goes into record making and record keeping. The average district general hospital holds about 200,000 sets of case notes. Between 10,000 and 20,000 of these will be in use in any one month. About 15 per cent of health care costs arise from handling records (Audit Commission, 1995a): about £10 million per NHS trust per year (Benson, 1997). However, this does not take into account the fact that doctors and nurses spend just over one quarter of their working time composing and scrutinising records (Audit Commission, 1995b). Social workers who mainly assess clients' and carers' needs probably spend a larger percentage of their time doing this (Department of Health, 1994a). People who work in the Benefits Agency do little else but make and consult records. As you saw from Unit 18, locality planning systems also generate large and extensive records in the form of minutes of meetings, bids for finance, community care and locality commissioning plans, contracts and monitoring reports.

By contrast, some people who work in health and social care, such as care assistants in some residential homes, spend very little time reading records and make very few records themselves. Nonetheless, there will be records concerning them and their activities. For care assistants, for example, the kinds of records made in a residential home will define

The average district general hospital holds about 200,000 sets of case notes

their jobs and will be evidence about what they have done. And in some residential homes, such as Liberty of Earley House (see Unit 8), care assistants are quite heavily involved in record making. The category of people in health and social care who do the least in the way of recording are those who receive the services. And records about them are central to the workings of health and social care organisations.

Section 1 of this unit looks at the different functions records perform in health and social care. By showing what is done through making records it answers the question of why records are important.

Section 2 raises the issue of who should be enabled to enter information into the records of an organisation. What role should the users of services play in this? Linked to this is the matter of writing records to be comprehensible and useful to the people who use them. These issues in turn hinge on what the records concerned are for. Access to the process of making records and client-friendly forms of recording are important where making and using records can be useful to the people who receive health and care services. Section 2 considers this.

Section 3 extends the discussion about who should have access to records by considering privacy and confidentiality of information. Section 4 examines the limits of confidentiality, when the health and safety of some people require the disclosure of private information about others.

The Conclusion rounds off the unit by reviewing the way in which the core questions have been addressed. However, the unit does not exhaust all that will be said about recording in this block. As you will see, one of the most important functions of recording is to make people accountable for their actions. Accountability is the topic of Unit 20. Confidentiality features again in Unit 21, the skills unit for this block.

Core questions

- What functions do records and recording perform in health and social care organisations?

- What do the users of services need from records and how can recording best serve their needs?

- How can those about whom information is recorded control the way it is shared?

- How can a balance be struck between respecting the privacy of one individual by keeping recorded information confidential, and protecting the interests of others who may have a legitimate need to know this information?

Section 1
The functions of recording in health and care

This section looks at the different functions that records perform in health and social care. It does so by looking first at a 'care plan', which is one of the most common kinds of record to be found in health and care practice. It then goes on to consider the relationship between the *process* of making records and the *product* of this, which is the record itself.

1.1   A care plan as a record

The term 'care plan' is widely used in health and care contexts. But what are called 'care plans' vary greatly. Not only do the care plans made by nurses or social workers or physiotherapists and so on vary, but so do those made by social workers in different authorities or by nurses working in different hospitals. These differences are partly due to agencies trying to solve the same problems of recording information, but finding different ways of doing so. And they are partly due to the fact that what needs to be put in a care plan depends very much on who is going to read it, and what use they are going to make of it. Thus a nursing care plan written to co-ordinate the activities of nurses on a ward will necessarily be different from a care plan written by a social worker as a way of defining the service which has been purchased from a home care agency. You saw an example of the latter in Unit 3, when you looked at the care plan for Alice to be carried out by staff from Independent Nursing Services.

So the care plan you are going to look at here is not necessarily typical or representative of all the documents which are called 'care plans'. Similarly, no general rules can be made against which care plans can be judged as good or bad. Of course, you can make judgements about whether the care outlined in the plan is appropriate or not, but that's judging the care rather than the care plan. When it comes to deciding the adequacy of a care plan *as a record*, you first need to ask questions about what, exactly, this care plan is trying to do. Then you can decide how well it does it.

Activity 1   A care plan for Arthur Durrant

Allow about 10 minutes

Offprint 27 shows the kind of care plan which might have been written for Arthur Durrant shortly after his discharge from hospital, by Dev Sharma, the social worker who acts as care (or case) manager for him. You met Arthur Durrant and his daughter Lynne in Block 1 of this course. For this activity read through the care plan and make some notes about what you think its purposes are. You might start by considering who seems to be the reader the plan is written for.

Comment   At first sight, at least, the plan seems to be written for Arthur to read. The term 'you' meaning 'Arthur' is used. It tells Arthur what services it has been agreed will be provided. In that sense the care plan is a set of promises to Arthur: a kind of contract such that if these promises are broken he will have grounds to complain. Note that the plan says that Arthur has been given a copy of the departmental complaints procedures. Where records make promises, they make those who make the promises accountable for keeping them. *Making people accountable* is often an important function of records. It means setting them up for judgement as to whether they have behaved properly.

The plan also describes some actions which have been taken by Dev Sharma: for example, that he has arranged for an occupational therapist to visit, and that he has checked Arthur's welfare benefits situation. These are actions a good social worker should have taken, so in this way the plan shows that Dev has done what he should have done. If his manager looked at the plan this would be apparent. So the plan not only makes Dev and the social services department accountable to Arthur, but also makes Dev accountable to his employers. Since this plan is only a tiny portion of a very large set of records about Arthur (and Lynne) it also makes Dev accountable for having designed a care plan appropriate to whatever the other records show.

In the plan Dev Sharma makes promises on behalf of the social services department. In that sense he *authorises* social services expenditure. As a care manager he may have a budget to spend (Downey, 1995) or he may have had to apply to his senior for permission to spend money on buying in home care services. Either way, this care plan *authorises* social services expenditure. Arthur's signature at the end also gives authorisation. It says, 'I agree to this package of care'.

In fact, a great deal on the form is outside Dev Sharma's authority. He has no power to commit the housing department, the community nursing services, the consultant in charge of diabetes, hospital transport or the wheelchair technicians. The last four belong to the health service, not to social services. So those entries on the plan merely report what other people have agreed to do. The official guidance for social care assessment (Department of Health, 1991a; Northern Ireland Office, 1991) makes social workers responsible not only for assessing their clients' needs for social care but for other services as well. Look at the bottom of the form. There is a circulation list which includes other practitioners and other agencies. Circulating this plan to these others ensures that it performs a function of *co-ordination*. It tells everyone involved what has been agreed with Arthur – which is something they all need to know.

A large number of care plans like this would also be useful for *monitoring* what was happening in the disability care team of which Dev Sharma is a member. Records are often used as the basis for monitoring how an agency is performing. You encountered this idea as 'management information' in Unit 18.

So, although the plan looks as if it was written just for Arthur to read, it also assumes other readers, particularly where it has a function of accountability, authorisation, co-ordination and monitoring.

 This care plan would only be a small part of the documentation concerning Arthur's care. For example, it would have resulted from a 'community care assessment' conducted by Dev Sharma and the social services occupational therapist and perhaps other social services employees such as the hospital social worker. The forms for community care assessments usually run to between 15 and 30 pages, although not all pages would be relevant to all clients. The differences between authorities here depend more on the size of print rather than on differences of content (Department of Health, 1994a). The box shows a breakdown of the kinds of information sought and recorded for a community care assessment for an older person, or for an adult with a disability. The assessing social workers have considerable discretion about what information they record, but as you scan through the items in the box you will realise that some of these items will be highly relevant for some service users, so that missing any of them might be dangerous for someone. Had Arthur's assessment occurred after April 1996 Lynne would have been eligible for a separate assessment of her needs as a carer, under the Carers (Recognition and Services) Act 1995. Since she was already a client of social services in her own right, they might have dispensed with this.

Information which might be recorded in a community care assessment for older people and adults with disabilities or mental health problems

- Social services or social work file number

- Health service case number

- Name, aliases, age, date of birth, gender, ethnic group, religion, marital status, dependent children, address, previous addresses, telephone numbers

- Need for interpreters/translators

- Previous contact with social services in this or another authority

- Relatives who are clients of social services

- Registered as disabled person or not

- Next of kin (relationship, address, contact point), co-residents/informal carers (relationship to client). Liable relatives (who can be charged for social care services). Key holders if person lives alone

- Care group (e.g. Elderly Care, Learning Disabilities, Mental Health)

- GP (fund-holder or not fund-holder), name, contact number

- Other agencies involved in the client's care and contact names/numbers

- Source of referral, date of referral

- Employment/unemployment

- Current accommodation circumstances: owner occupier/kind of tenancy, etc.

- Suitability of accommodation: heating, lighting, cooking, access to toilet, access to bathroom/shower, access to premises, dampness, safety, security

- Sensory impairment: vision, hearing, speech impairment

- Mobility (as assessed by occupational therapist if necessary): assistance required with getting into/out of bed, into/out of chair. Able to walk so far/unable to walk. Able/unable to climb stairs. Uses/requires stick, zimmer, wheelchair, stairlift, ramps, hoists, two staff to lift. Able/unable to leave house without assistance. Has/requires specially adapted vehicle

- Daily pattern of activities

- Health as described by doctor. Medical history or referral to doctor if appropriate

- Use of medicines and other medical equipment (e.g. oxygen cylinders)

- Continence: of bladder, of bowels. Pattern of incontinence
- Psychological state (as assessed by psychiatrist/psychologist if necessary): lucid/limited comprehension; confused/depressed. Psychiatric history if any. Requirement for psychiatric or counselling referral
- Prostheses: dentures, glasses, other. Requires/receives assistance in using
- Personal care: washes unaided/needs assistance. Dresses unaided/needs assistance. Needs medical assistance (for catheters or wound dressing, etc.)
- Food and drink: fully independent/needs assistance with eating. Able/unable to cater for self. Receives/needs meals on wheels or other arrangements for feeding. Special dietary needs and preferences
- Evidence of behavioural problems (as assessed by psychiatrist/psychologist if appropriate): memory loss, wandering, anxiety, physical aggression, verbal aggression, hoarding, restlessness, challenging behaviour, inappropriate sexual behaviour. Drug or alcohol problems. Supervised discharge (in Scotland community care order). Entered on supervision register (England only)
- Criminal record. Status in criminal justice system: ex-offender, probation, parole, case pending, etc.
- Legal status: nationality, child/ward of court/power of attorney/enduring power of attorney, guardianship order/other court of protection order. Name of person acting on behalf of client. Location of will and other key legal documents
- Financial status: capital, income, necessary expenditure, benefits eligible for, benefits actually receiving. Liability to pay for social care
- Preference on death (for older clients or terminally ill clients): cremation/burial. Christian/Jewish/Muslim/Hindu/secular/other funeral
- Risk assessment: kind of risk (e.g. falls, wandering, self-neglect, aggression to others), degree of risk (high, medium, low). Measures required to minimise risk
- Client's biography and health and care history
- Client's daily activities
- Client's domestic relationships and social network
- Client's perception of own situation/client's particular concerns
- Client's desires with regard to accommodation, mobility, assistance in the home, social relationships, leisure activities, spiritual needs, training, education, occupation
- Carer's ability to care and need for assistance, including need for respite care
- Other records/practitioners consulted
- Name of assessing practitioner(s). Date, duration and location of assessment

From the contents of the box you will see that records of community care assessments will contain much more information than Arthur's care plan. This is the kind of information which forms the basis for making decisions. Arthur's care plan was written when most of the decisions about his care had been made for the time being. In this sense it wasn't typical of those many kinds of records which have the function of *collating and storing information for decision making*. Medical records are perhaps the best example of records having this kind of function, particularly where they record the results of examinations and diagnostic tests. You will also see from the box that records from other sources enter into the community care assessments conducted by social workers: for example medical records, records of immigration status, court orders (about guardianship for example) and records of psychological or psychiatric assessments. Equally, the community care assessment may have consequences for recording elsewhere. For example, it may generate records in the housing department, may cause medical records to be added to, and so on. The next activity asks you to think about the way in which one kind of record often links in with another kind.

Activity 2   **Records linking with records**

Allow about 15 minutes

Look back at Arthur's care plan (Offprint 27) and see if you can guess what other kinds of records led up to this plan of care, and what others are likely to exist in parallel with it.

To begin the list you can write down Arthur's community care assessment discussed above.

Comment   Here are some possibilities for the records which *preceded* the care plan.

First, there is the community care assessment conducted by social services, and this involved reference to Arthur's records at the Benefits Agency and, directly or indirectly, to Arthur's medical records. Presumably, Lynne's social services records would also play a part. Then there were records made by the occupational therapist in doing an assessment of the need for home adaptations. There were the Durrants' records in the housing department. Arthur's medical records, and especially the additions made by the consultant in diabetes, will have been directly relevant to the GP's plans for Arthur, and to the regime involving the community nursing sister.

The records important *in parallel* with Arthur's plan of care will include the community nursing sister's own care plan for Arthur, which she will have worked out either with the consultant or with the GP. The prescriptions issued by the GP will generate records which will debit the practice's budget for drugs and become part of the income of a pharmacist. Since Arthur has diabetes and is on a low income, he will not be paying prescription charges, so there will be records concerning his exemption from this (Department of Health, 1996b). There will be records of the outpatients' clinic and the records of the hospital transport service. Arthur's records at the Benefits Agency will now include his newly awarded disability living allowance. Somewhere there will be records which instruct someone to pay this to him. There will be a contract between the social services department and Care at Home, and probably a care plan specially for Doreen, Arthur's home care assistant, saying what she should (and should not) do for him. The approach to the housing department will probably result in a visit from a housing officer, which again will be recorded. Arthur had to sign for his wheelchair, and wheelchair maintenance is contracted out; so another contract for this. The wheelchair will already have been serviced and the technician will have documented this. Depending on what they are, the home adaptations might be paid for by the housing department or by the social services department. Either way the specifications will be recorded and contracts placed to have the work done. Payments will be made and this will generate invoices and records of expenditure. The cost of delivering Arthur's care plan will have to be accounted for in the financial records of the social services department. And since Arthur makes a financial contribution towards his home care there will be an entry for him in a system for issuing bills and collecting receipts.

It is probably just as well to stop at this point, because if you go any further you will be tracing records down routes which grow more and more branches. Just think of following the trail from Doreen's job with Arthur to her time sheets, her contract of employment, her tax and national insurance record, and so on. Or following the records of the hospital transport system down the branches which deal with insurance, vehicle maintenance, staff training, and so on. The point is that records made in one context very often have implications for records made in another.

You have now looked at five functions which records might perform: accountability, authorisation, constituting information for decision making, or information for monitoring performance, and providing information to co-ordinate the activities of different people. A record rarely performs only one of these functions and in practice the same record may perform many of them all at the same time. Table 1 presents the same ideas in a more formal way. It also adds two other functions for records you haven't considered so far in this unit.

Table 1   Some functions of record making

Functions	*Examples*
1 Accountability *Records may say who is responsible for doing what, and what they have (or haven't) done, and hence be a means of judging people.*	The kinds of records kept by residential homes are good examples: the residential home is required to do certain things and the records say whether these things have been done. At the end of any form of application for welfare benefits there will be a section where the claimant is asked to sign that the details filled in on the form are accurate. The signature makes the claimant accountable for the honesty of the claim: there are fines and prison sentences for false claims.
2 Authorisation *Records may indicate who has a right, and perhaps a duty, to do what with regard to whom.*	The best example is probably the record that someone has consented to an operation or some other medical intervention: this authorises health personnel to carry out the operation. Other examples include references and education certificates used in gaining employment; assessment forms which record the eligibility of someone to receive a benefit or service; a 'letter of administration' or 'power of attorney', which allows a person to manage someone else's financial affairs when they are unable to do so.

3 Decision making about service users *Records may assemble and store the information on which decisions about clients should be based and information about decisions which have been made.*	Any record of a diagnostic test – an x-ray photograph for example – and other medical records, and virtually all records about clients of social services, such as assessment forms.
4 Monitoring the performance of services *Records may assemble and store information about how and how well an organisation is performing.*	Difficult to distinguish from the above, but the kinds of records which show how many people visit an agency; what kinds of people receive what kind of treatment; what the gender and ethnic mix of the client group is; the case loads of the workers; how many violent incidents happen each year; how many clients achieve satisfactory outcomes.
5 Co-ordinating activities *Records may indicate who should be doing what and when so that people can gear their activities one with another.*	Care plans which involve care delivered by more than one person or agency; referral forms and letters from one agency to another; contracts between purchasers and providers.
6 Systematic practice *Record making makes practice systematic.*	The kinds of forms filled in by a social worker when assessing the financial situation of a client tells the social worker what questions to ask. In this sense it structures his or her perceptions of what is relevant, and organises what the social worker does. Forms and checklists like this are common in record-making systems in health and care work.
7 Reflection, personal growth and/or professional development, and as means of making relationships *Making a record makes sense of an experience or a situation. In making a record two people get to know each other.*	In the Introduction and Study Guide it was suggested you keep a learning diary. Some practitioners keep diaries which they use as the basis for reflecting on their practice. Life history books (Unit 14) are an obvious example. Looking together at a life history book can be a successful way to develop a relationship between service user and worker.

1.2 Process and product in record making

The last two functions on the list are rather different from the other five. For these two the *process* of making the record is at least as important as the record which is made.

Referring to the last function in Table 1, Jamie, whom you met in Unit 14, is proud of his life history book and would probably be devastated if he lost it. But the thinking and the feeling and the social interaction involved in making life history books are probably more important than the book itself. In a related area – adult literacy work – students often write biographical accounts. These sometimes lead to publishable stories, but the main purpose of writing the accounts is learning to write (Atkinson and Williams, 1990). In some respects reminiscence work and other autobiographical recording is like most of the activities you are asked to do in this course. The notes you produce as answers – the product – are far less important than what you learned in writing them – the process.

Activity 3   **Activities and TMAs**

Allow about 10 minutes   Think about the difference between the activities in K100, such as this one, and the TMAs you have completed. Both involve recording information. But how do they differ? Use Table 1 to identify what function TMAs perform as records which your responses to the activities do not.

Comment   First, your responses to activities are personal to you. They don't get into the records of The Open University at all. The only functions they can perform are the 'process' ones (6 and 7 in Table 1). Doing them is supposed to serve as a means for achieving something else: promoting your learning in this case. Some activities are set up so as to structure the way you go about learning. They aim to fulfil the sixth function in the table. TMAs, of course, are designed for the same purposes, but because you send them to a tutor they can perform additional functions as well.

For function 1 in Table 1, TMAs make you *accountable* in the sense that they allow judgements to be made about what you have learnt, how well you can write, and so on. You are required to get your TMAs in on time, so they also make you accountable for this. They make your tutor accountable for marking the TMAs, and in due time. Although you don't see this, tutor marking is monitored by other staff at the OU, so tutors become accountable in terms of the appropriateness and accuracy of their marking. The monitors also make records of their monitoring, and these make them accountable for showing they have done their jobs as monitors adequately.

Function 2. Your TMAs are the basis for the marks you receive. They are the evidence which *authorises* you to be given marks towards the final score which makes you the authorised owner of so many CATS points.

Function 3. The TMAs and other records made about them store information which forms the basis for *decisions* made by your tutor or at examination board meetings.

Function 4. Everyone's TMAs together provide the basis for the University to *monitor* whether the TMAs were appropriately set, accurately marked and so on.

Function 5. The sets of TMAs looked at by those who monitor marking standards allow monitors to give advice to tutors so that everyone's marking is *co-ordinated* around the same standards.

In the course of all this, information about your TMAs gets transformed into records of other kinds, most of which you will never see, and probably have no need to see.

Study skills: Making use of assignments and activities

What you have just read is highly relevant to your skills as a student. Apart from the important roles that TMAs perform within the OU system (Table 1, functions 1 to 5), they play a vital part in helping you to learn. By making you write down a 'record' of what is in your head, TMAs:

- require you to *make sense* of what you have been reading (rather than have it floating around half-formed in your head) (function 7).

- help to *systematise* your practice as a student, making you plough ahead through the course material to find out what you need to know for the assignment and encouraging you to make notes and then organise them (function 6).

- provide the basis of a *relationship* with your tutor, through which he or she can respond to your ideas and help you develop them, as well as help develop your skills as a writer (function 7).

This is why you need to treat assignments as a core part of the learning process and set aside plenty of time for them.

Similarly, *activities* in the text help to systematise your study practice and require you to make sense of what you read rather than becoming hypnotised by the words – this is why it is important not to skip them and just read the answers.

Equally, you can think of *note taking* as 'writing a record' of your studies. It has the same 'process' effects, turning reading into a more structured activity and forcing you to make sense as you go along. It also provides 'evidence' that you have studied, which can be very cheering when you begin to wonder whether you are making any progress at all. Writing records always takes an effort, but it can help you exert control over the mysterious learning processes that go on deep in your mind.

Using forms

If you look back at the box in Section 1.1 which lists the kinds of matters recorded in a community care assessment, or indeed in an assessment for residential care, you will probably agree that without a form (proforma) to fill in it would be virtually impossible for the practitioner to remember all the questions that his or her agency thinks need answering. In terms of function 6 in Table 1, a proforma forces the practitioner to do an assessment in a way that *systematically* collects all the information the agency thinks is relevant to decision making (function 3).

Good examples of forms which force practitioners into systematic practice are the kinds of charts nurses have to fill in to record temperature or continence (see the continence chart overleaf). Most such charts can easily be read to see whether practitioners have done what they should have done. For example, a temperature chart shows whether temperatures have indeed been taken when a nurse was instructed to take them. The continence chart shows clearly how often the nurse monitored the continence of the patient, and in providing a set of symbols shows what it is the nurse should be looking for and recording. Thus charts like this tell practitioners what to do, and show whether they have done it.

CONTINENCE PROMOTION CHART												Mr Kay
	ASSESSMENT											
TIME \ DAY	1 Sept 10		2 Sept 11		3 Sept 12		4 Sept 13		5 Sept 14		6	7	8	9	10
00.00															
01.00															
02.00					○		○	□	○	□					
03.00															
04.00									●	■					
05.00			●	▲	●	■	●	■							
06.00									○	□					
07.00	●	■													
08.00			●	■					●	■					
09.00					○										
10.00	●	□	●	▲			○	□							
11.00	○								○	□					
12 Midday			○												
13.00	●	▲	●	▲	●	■			●	□					
14.00									○						
15.00					○										
16.00	●	▲	●	▲			○	□	○	□					
17.00															
18.00															
19.00	●	■	●	■	●	■									
20.00							○	□	○	□					
21.00	●	□	●	□											
22.00	○	□	○	□	○	□									
23.00															

KEY:

Incontinent ○	Aid offered – urine not passed □	Asked for aid, did not use △
Continent ●	Aid offered – urine passed ■	Asked for aid, urine passed ▲ Absent ✗

A continence promotion chart. Some forms of recording in health and social care force practitioners to practise in a systematic way. For example, this chart indicates what the nurse should be looking for by providing symbols for recording, and it shows how often the nurse assessed the continence of the patient

Comparing functions 6 and 7 in Table 1 suggests a contradiction between, on the one hand, the aim of systematically recording everything that a service organisation needs to know about a service user (6), and on the other, allowing service users the latitude to decide what they think is relevant and important about themselves (7). Form filling may get in the way of developing productive relationships between service users and workers.

Activity 4 **For and against forms in making records**

Allow about 15 minutes For this activity think about the use of forms by practitioners in making records about service users. Suppose you had to go and collect information about and from someone. Would you prefer to use a pre-prepared form or not? Make two lists. One list should be the benefits of using a form and the other should be the disadvantages. For your lists think about the collection of information *and* about social relationships and feelings.

Comment

Advantages of using a form	Disadvantages of using a form
More likely that the necessary information will be collected	Form may not allow for collection of some information most important to service user
On a form other practitioners will know where to find the information they want	Reshapes unique details of service user into same standard format
Easy to transform into computerised record system (if not input directly into such a system)	Inhibits practitioners from responding to service users as unique individuals
Separates different kinds of information for separate circulation on a need-to-know basis	Restricts interaction to question-and-answer routine
Imposes standardised performance on practitioners – equality of treatment for each service user	Recording may be experienced as intrusive and disempowering
Well-designed forms pose clear questions	Standardised questions may inhibit practitioners from following up issues which are important to the client
Practitioners unlikely to forget important questions, therefore may feel more secure	Can be experienced by practitioners as de-skilling and over-controlling

The two lists in the comment suggest that whether forms are advantageous or disadvantageous really depends on three considerations:

1   what the service user wants from the interaction
2   how the practitioner behaves in eliciting the information
3   for what purpose the record is being made.

If the service user wants to develop a highly personalised relationship with a practitioner, then filling in forms might get in the way. But that applies only if developing a highly personalised relationship was a possibility in the first place. And not all service users want deep, meaningful relationships with practitioners. A course tester with personal experience of being a user of mental health services wrote:

> *I much prefer the process where my doctor keys information into the computer. I can see exactly what he is recording about me and it's there for me to correct or ask questions about if I want to. I don't like people talking to me and then going away and writing things down, because then I don't know what they will have written.*

I also like to be asked clear questions. It worries me if professionals try engage me in what seems like an informal conversation, because I know they are angling to get information out of me, but I don't know what. I don't think that's a fair way to treat patients.

This tester found the computer screen interaction with her doctor preferable to:

... people trying to develop deep meaningful relationships with you in half an hour and then disappearing out of your life entirely. With the form-filling kind of interaction, at least there is no pretence that friendship and support are being offered, when the person concerned isn't in a position to offer it.

Regarding the practitioner's attitude in eliciting information, a highly structured form doesn't necessarily imply an impersonal, standardised approach. Indeed, if you look again at Offprint 27 you will see that, although the care plan is written on a form, it seems to assume that some unstructured discussion takes place before the form is completed, or at the very least, before Arthur signs it.

Whether it is best to use forms for record making depends on the purpose of the record. Looking again at the comment to Activity 4, it seems likely that most people would regard a form as a worthwhile device if its purpose was to record information necessary for, say, obtaining a bank overdraft, booking a holiday or applying for a welfare benefit. On the other hand, most people would probably find a form inhibiting in a situation where the purpose was to form a friendship, counsel someone contemplating suicide or help someone write up their autobiography.

In Unit 14 you considered the value of reminiscence work and of the kinds of records which arise from this, such as life history books. Such work gives service users the opportunity to appraise their own lives and learn that their lives can be interesting to other people. It also provides others with information and understanding which they can use in making relationships with the service user. A structured approach in this area would obviously be inappropriate. However, for the vast majority of people, encounters with health and social care services are relatively short-term and necessarily shallow. The kind of information which needs to be recorded is not of the kind on which deep, lasting personal relationships are based. Rather, it is the kind of information used to make immediate and practical decisions. Does this person need a hip replacement operation? Is this person sufficiently disabled to warrant providing home care services? Are they liable to make a financial contribution towards this? These are the kinds of questions which practitioners have to ask all the time and record answers to. The advantages listed in the comment to Activity 4 suggest that forms are efficient tools for collecting this kind of information, assuming of course that the form asks the right questions.

1.3 Different purposes: different records

The important point arising from the discussion above is that what are appropriate processes and formats for making records depends on what purpose the record is supposed to fulfil. You can consider this further through the next activity.

Activity 5 Criteria for judging records

Allow about 15 minutes

For this activity use Table 2, which is a transformation of Table 1, to evaluate 'Eventide's shift log'. This is a page from one of the kinds of shift logs or hand-over books which are often used in residential homes for staff to communicate with each other. In evaluating it, first decide what purpose the log is supposed to serve, and then decide how well it does so.

Table 2 Functions and criteria for evaluating records

Functions	*Criteria*
If the function is to:	*Then the record should:*
1 Make people accountable	Show clearly who is committed to doing what, and who has done what – to the extent that the people who are intended to read the record need to know this
2 Authorise someone or some agency to do something	Show clearly who has the right to do what – to the extent that the people intended to read the record need to know this
3 Record the information necessary for making decisions concerning service users	Accurately record the information which is relevant to making the decisions – to the extent to which those making the decisions need to have this recorded
4 Record information to monitor how, and how well, an organisation is working	Accurately record information which is appropriate evidence of whatever aspect of performance is being monitored. Remember your work in specifying monitoring data for a meals-on-wheels service in Unit 18
5 Provide the basis for co-ordinating activity between different people and different agencies	Clearly indicate who should be doing what and when; who (if anyone) has the role of co-ordinating this; to whom information should be circulated – to the extent to which those involved need to have this recorded
6 Make practice systematic	Be compiled in a format which forces practitioners to ask all the relevant questions/consider all the information relevant to making the decision
7 Make sense of an experience or a situation as part of a process of personal or professional development; or as a way of making a relationship	Be made through a process which allows for the individual concerned to record what they think is most relevant and important, allowing time for them to consider and reconsider this and/or through a process which fosters trust and mutual understanding

Eventide's shift log

27th March	From Marion: Mrs Shelly died in the night. Please tell all residents as you get them up. She died 'peacefully'.
	If Mr Turner takes a nap, please put up the bed rail. He will object, but we have agreed this with his daughter. Mrs Tulley's birthday – cards in my office – please take to her. Plumber is coming to look at radiator in number 21
8·30	Plumber arrived before Mrs Evans was up.!!! – bit of aggro because I wouldn't let him in (JK). Went off without doing his job.
9.15	Mrs Evans concerned about her pills – only enough left for two days – and her face powder – enough for months – and her HA batteries!
10.32	Mr Prout more confused than usual. Insisted Jean was his daughter. Asked her to take him home. Carpet tile loose on top landing: have Sellotaped it for now.
11.35	Warning! Mr Prout has a bottle of Whiskey!!!!!! V. low on disposable razors.

Comment   The prime and almost only function which the Eventide shift log fulfils is co-ordination. This is the way in which the staff of the home convey information to each other. At first sight it may appear as a very unsystematic set of jottings. But if its only purpose is for staff to give messages to each other, when they can't do this face to face, then it probably works quite well. Note that Table 2 contains several clauses to the effect that records only need to record matters 'to the extent that the people who are intended to read the record need to know'. These staff know who is the occupant of room 21 and that Mr Prout is troublesome when he has been drinking. These matters don't have to be spelt out in detail.

You could argue that staff in the home should be collecting and recording much more information about the health and morale of the residents. In fact, in this particular home such information is collected, but by the qualified nursing staff, either directly from the residents or by asking the care assistant. Such information is entered in the residents' personal files, where its confidentiality is more secure, and not in the shift log. You could also argue that the shift log should make care assistants and the home itself more accountable by giving a detailed account of what the staff do on each shift. Your reading of Reader Chapter 25 'Bedroom abuse' in Unit 4 might have suggested this, or you might have considered that such information would be valuable for the inspection of residential and nursing homes (Unit 8): functions 1 and 4 in Table 1. This may be true but the important point here is that you cannot judge how adequate a record or a recording system is until you have decided what it is for, and if the shift log is only intended for co-ordinating staff activities when they can't do this face to face, then it probably works well enough.

In judging whether records are good, bad or indifferent then, it is important first to decide what they are for. For example, in Unit 16 it was noted with some regret that the records of Lennox Castle did not provide a detailed picture of what it was like to live in such an institution. But contributing to the historical record wasn't what Lennox Castle records were designed to do. One kind of record featured in the video was the reports by visitors from the Board of Control which inspected such institutions. The records of misdemeanours and punishments would have been an important document for inspection teams to scrutinise. Having to record the punishments and deprivations meted out to residents was part of an attempt to make such behaviour 'above board' and inspectable, such that staff would have to give reasons for punishing and show that punishments were proportionate to the offence. These then are records which primarily serve the function of making the institution accountable to a body charged with overseeing the welfare of inmates. These days the case notes on individual residents would be regarded as based on erroneous ideas about learning disability. But in terms of their own time they are punctilious records of what was regarded as information relevant to the care and control of such people. They were 'good' records, but based on 'bad' ideas. It is quite likely that at least some of the kinds of records today regarded as 'good practice' will in the future be regarded as based on erroneous theories.

The next activity asks you, in effect, to repeat Activity 5, but this time for Arthur Durrant's care plan.

Activity 6   **Evaluating Arthur's care plan as a record**

Allow about 15 minutes

Look again at Arthur's care plan (Offprint 27) and at Table 2. Think again about what functions this record is supposed to perform and then decide how well it performs them. For the functions you might like to look again at the comment to Activity 1.

Comment   Remembering the clauses about recording only to the extent to which the readers of the records need the information, then Arthur's care plan seems to rate quite well with regard to the criteria in Table 2 for accountability (1), authorisation (2) and co-ordination (5). The information for decision making (3) is mainly recorded elsewhere; the care plan is the result of considering this information. It is not a particularly good record for monitoring the performance of services (4). But that is not its purpose. Using a form has forced Dev Sharma to look systematically at Arthur's accommodation needs, health needs, social needs and so on, making it less likely that some area of need will be missed (6). It is doubtful whether the care plan itself contributes to Arthur's personal growth and development, or to creating a good relationship (7), but these would depend on how Dev Sharma handled the discussion leading up to the plan.

From the last two activities you should have seen that it is difficult to make general statements about what constitute 'good' records. Records are made for different purposes, so good practice depends on what the purpose of making the record is. Adequate records for pinning down accountability are not necessarily good records for making decisions about care. And good records for reminiscence work are certainly not good records for establishing whether someone is eligible for a particular service and hence can be authorised to receive it. Imagine trying to operate a welfare benefits system where applications were made through presenting life history books. A recording system adequately fulfilling all the functions listed in Table 1 to the same degree would be much too expensive to operate. Perhaps a good general question to ask about any kind of record is, 'Does it record what the readers of the records need to know in terms of the purpose the record is supposed to fulfil, *and no more than this*?'

1.4 Appropriate investment in record making

The 'no more than this' is important in two ways: one relating to expense and the other to privacy and confidentiality. The matter of confidentiality is dealt with later in the unit but, as you saw from the first section, making and curating records is extremely expensive. In 1994 the Social Services Inspectorate (Department of Health, 1994a) reported with some alarm that community care assessments under the terms of the NHS and Community Care Act 1990 were sometimes taking five hours or more to complete. When social services and social work departments fulfil their obligations to assess carers under the Carers (Recognition and Services) Act 1995, they will be spending even more time in making records (Watson and Taylor, 1996).

In health and social care there is a built-in demand for more and more record making. One way of understanding this is to reconsider what is listed in Tables 1 and 2. Whatever the problem is, there is a tendency to seek a solution by recording more information. Thus, if practitioners or agencies are thought not to be sufficiently *accountable* to those they serve, a solution is sought in making more records which specify more closely what has been promised, and record what has been done. For example the Patient's Charter (Department of Health 1991b, 1995b), which makes promises to patients, is accompanied by a requirement to make records to show how far health agencies have kept these promises (McIver and Martin, 1996).

Similarly, if anti-discriminatory practice (Unit 12) is to mean anything, it requires records to be made, in terms of which it can be *monitored*; ethnic monitoring records are an example. Again, if practitioners are thought sometimes to act beyond their own authority, disempowering service users, then a solution is looked for in getting service users to sign agreements to *authorise* treatments or care packages. Everybody wants *decisions* about health and social care to be based on the best possible evidence, so there is always a demand that practitioners collect more evidence for decision making. This is particularly marked in the health service where 'evidence-based medicine' is regarded as a way of improving the quality of care and the efficiency of resource use (National Health Service Executive, 1996b; Walshe and Ham, 1997). What evidence-based medicine means is that treatments should be chosen on the basis of evidence that they work. That means collecting evidence to see whether treatments do work, and looking at each case for evidence that a particular treatment is likely to work – and of course, recording all this.

Again, hope has been placed in better management as a way of improving the performance of health and social services. But to manage, managers need information to *monitor* what is happening. The main way in which they get information is through their staff spending time recording what they do, or contractors spending time recording the information needed to monitor their compliance with their contract (Unit 18). Concern about standards in residential care usually leads to suggestions that inspections should be more rigorous (Unit 8). More rigorous inspection would mean more records made by the residential establishments for inspection teams to look at, and more records made by the inspection teams themselves. And, as noted in Unit 18, health and social care services, defined in the broadest sense, are poorly *co-ordinated*. So there is a demand that they plan together at the strategic level, and record their deliberations and conclusions. And there is a demand that they *co-ordinate* more effectively with one another in providing packages of care for individual service users by making and sharing records which tell each other what they are doing. Then, from a rather different direction, there is a demand that service users should be treated as the unique individuals they are, and that for this purpose records should be produced through biographical or autobiographical approaches (Unit 16 and function 7 on Tables 1 and 2). Such approaches have the potential to generate very weighty records indeed and are a long time in the making.

In the face of all these demands for more records there is a demand that health and social care services spend less time on paperwork and more time on direct care. This demand often comes from the same people who are, in effect, asking for more recording to be done. Taken one at a time, each case suggested above for making more, and more detailed, records is usually quite convincing. But proceeding on all these fronts at the same time very quickly leads to two practical problems. First, if health and social care practitioners spend more time recording, they cannot spend as much time doing other things. Second, the more there is recorded, the longer the records take to consult, and the less likely it is that people will find the time to use the information which has been recorded.

The difficulty of deciding what is 'the minimum necessary' to record lies in the fact that different groups make different demands on systems of recording. Governments, managers (of different kinds), auditors, different kinds of practitioners, workplace trainers, researchers, regulatory bodies, equal opportunities committees, organised groups of service users, individual service users and informal carers may all want different matters recorded and more of this and less of that.

Key points

- Records may fulfil a number of different functions in health and social care.

- Sometimes the process of collecting the information to make the record may be more important than the record itself and sometimes the process may be a secondary consideration.

- Different purposes for records require different processes and formats for recording.

- Most records fulfil several functions at one and the same time, but a recording system which is ideal for one purpose may not be ideal for another.

- Since recording is costly, deciding what is the minimum necessary is an important matter, but since there are competing demands about what should be recorded, the minimum necessary is usually quite a lot.

Section 2

Records for service users and informal carers

An issue raised earlier (Activity 1) was the question of who the readers of records are intended to be. So far this unit has looked at recorded information mainly from the viewpoint of those who provide and manage the provision of care. This section looks at the ways in which recorded information might be useful to service users and informal carers.

2.1 What service users and carers might want from records

Traditionally, records in health and social care have been regarded primarily as tools for workers rather than as facilities for service users and their informal carers. But it is worth considering how records might be made in a way that is comprehensible to clients and carers, and useful to them.

Activity 7

Allow about 10 minutes

Records for service users and carers

Look again at functions 1 to 5 in Table 1. They are listed again below. Think of yourself as a service user or as an informal carer. For each of these five functions say to yourself: 'I want to know ...' and jot down some ideas about what you would want to know corresponding with each function. You might like to look again at Arthur's care plan to see how well it answers questions for him.

In terms of:

(a)   accountability

(b)   authority

(c)   information for decision making

(d)   information for monitoring the performance of services

(e)   co-ordination

I want to know ...

Comment

Here are some ideas:

(a)   *Accountability.* I want to know who has promised to do what, so that if I am dissatisfied I know what to complain about, who to complain about and how to complain. I want to know what the complaints procedures are. Arthur's care plan seems to include a great deal of this sort of information, saying who is going to do what, giving contact numbers, and recording that he has been given the social services complaints procedures booklet.

(b)   *Authorisation.* I want to know what my rights are, and I want to know who is authorised to do what in relation to me. For example, I want to know what staff are authorised to do with the information I give them (confidentiality is dealt with later in this unit). Arthur himself authorises the care plan by signing it. The plan does not tell him very much about who has the authority to do what.

(c) *Information for **my** decision making.* I should be given as much information as I want in order to make my own decisions. That includes being given information which I can understand. It is no good just telling me verbally. I want something written down so that I can look at it again and again, discuss it with other people, formulate questions about it, and so on. I also want information so that I can see how my treatment has progressed and how my condition has changed. I want to know what I can do for myself and how I can do it, and I want records which tell me how successful I have been. In Arthur's case most of the information for decision making is recorded elsewhere, in his medical records and in his social services assessment. There is no reason why he should not look at this information, but it is probable that there will be some of it which he doesn't understand. It is quite likely that the community nurse has given him some information about diabetes and about diets for diabetics.

(d) *Information for monitoring service performance.* I am most likely to want this kind of information if I belong to an organised group of service users and we have involved ourselves in monitoring the performance of services. For example, the Phoenix group from Unit 18 do a lot of this. For myself I might want to compare general practices before I decide which doctor to register with, or to compare home care agencies, particularly if I am going to pay for the service myself. People who receive direct payments to spend themselves rather than having services contracted for them by a care manager (Unit 3) would also benefit from this kind of information. Arthur's care plan doesn't give him any such information. That's not its purpose.

(e) *Information for co-ordination.* Unless services tell me who is supposed to be doing what and when and for what reasons, I won't be able to play a full part in my own care, or in the care of my relative or friend. This is much the same information as I need for services to make themselves accountable to me. As the notes under (a) above suggest, Arthur's care plan provides the information he needs in order to know who to contact if the co-ordination of his care package breaks down.

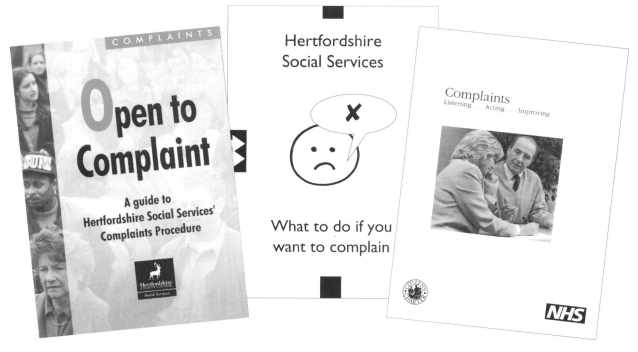

If services are to be accountable to service users, service users first need to know what they have a right to expect – written care plans help here – and then need to know how to complain when they don't get it. Complaints procedures have become much more accessible during the 1990s

2.2 Access to records

The information contained in records cannot be used by service users unless they have access to them. The Access to Health Records Act 1990 gives adult patients the right to see any health service records made about them after November 1991 (National Health Service Executive, 1991; Scottish Home and Health Department, 1989). When the European protocol on data protection is incorporated into British law in October 1998 it is likely that the 1991 cut-off date will disappear and patients will have the legal right to see records made about them whenever they were made (Department of Health, 1996a). The fact that patients don't have a legal right to see records made about them before 1991 doesn't necessarily mean that they would be refused access if they asked, and they can always gain access through a court order if the records are to be used as evidence. There are exceptions to rights of access, of which the following are the two most important.

- Doctors may refuse the patient access to all or part of the records if it is their medical opinion that access may 'cause serious physical or mental harm to the patient' (National Health Service Executive, 1991). This does not include situations in which the patient might be upset to learn that medical services had been negligent!

- Access may be denied if this would disclose information about a third party without his or her consent (National Health Service Executive, 1991). Third parties do not include doctors or others whose errors might be disclosed by a scrutiny of the records.

The law with regard to social services records is similar, although the relevant legislation is the Access to Personal Files Act 1987 (Social Work Services Group, 1989). The individual's rights to see his or her own records are reinforced through the Patient's Charter (Department of Health, 1991b; Unit 20), through the local Community Care Charters produced by social services or social work departments (Department of Health, 1994b), and through the Data Protection Act 1984. It often happens that, when there is a court case pending for medical negligence, patients (and their legal advisers) can gain access to the records only after a court order has been made against the trust, the GP or the dentist (Association of Community Health Councils for England and Wales, 1993), but the right to see one's own records is very well established in law. However, the records of health and social care are often incomprehensible to non-professionals.

2.3 Comprehensible records

People who receive health and social care services are often ill, confused or anxious, and their capacity to understand what is recorded about them may be limited. This is sometimes used as an excuse to withhold most of the documentation of health and social care from them entirely, unless they specifically ask for it, on the grounds that giving them more information would add to their burden, or that they would not understand the information anyway. But this policy is just as likely to add to their confusion and anxiety as it is to relieve it. Usually it is better to give people information so that they have a chance to understand it, than to withhold it on the assumption that they will not. This implies giving them the kind of information which they have the best chance of understanding. For people who are literate, written information is important as an adjunct to spoken information because they can review it at their own pace and in their own time. It would have been good practice to give Arthur a copy of his care plan some days before he signed it. Audio or videotaped information or pictograms (see Unit 14) can be used where service users have difficulty with literacy. Interpreters and translators may be necessary where people do not speak English, or have a visual or hearing impairment.

What you read about making information about services more 'user-friendly' in Unit 18 is equally applicable to making records more comprehensible to service users. There is, however, something of a conflict of intention between, on the one hand, making records which economically and efficiently convey information to practitioners and, on the other, making records which are comprehensible to service users. Practitioners have a head start. They don't need the meaning of technical terms explained to them. Nor, for example, do doctors and nurses have to be given a lesson on how the kidneys work in order to understand records about renal failure (Hammond, 1997).

On this issue the NHS Training Directorate says:

> It is not necessary or practical to expect health records to be written entirely in non-technical or 'lay' terminology. Professionals need to communicate with other professionals in professional terms. One suggestion to improve patient/client understanding is a 'patient-friendly' section – i.e. a summary of information previously discussed with the patient/client. As well as [reinforcing] their understanding of discussions, the summary also informs other health professionals what the patient knows about his/her condition, problems and care.
>
> (National Health Service Training Directorate, 1995, E6)

And, it might be added, while such summaries might not answer all the patient's questions, they would put a patient in a much better position to ask questions in future.

The National Health Service Training Directorate (1995, E7) also suggests glossaries explaining abbreviations and technical terms, and diagrams explaining how the body works on which the particular patient's condition can be indicated.

People wanting to find out more about a medical condition which appears in their records can make use of the national Health Information Service: freephone 0800 66 55 44.

Key points

- The right to access your own health or social care records is well established in law, although often service users don't seem to know they have these rights.

- Rights to access your own records don't amount to much if you can't understand the records when you look at them.

2.4 Records held by service users

Writing records for service users raises a question about *where* records ought to be kept. The more usual practice is for service user records to be banked with the service, making them inaccessible to the patient or client most of the time unless copies are made. And if the patient or client only has copies, these very quickly get separated from the process through which records are updated. So far the use of computer technology to handle records has served to reinforce the tendency for records to be centrally banked, since service users don't usually own the necessary computer hardware. Sometimes staff who work in satellite offices without terminals find that computer technology has separated them too from the records they need (Glastonbury, 1985).

 Arthur's care plan is, of course, a record held by a service user, and the official guidance for implementing the NHS and Community Care Act 1990 and its Northern Ireland equivalent (Department of Health, 1991a; Northern Ireland Office, 1991) recommends clients being given written care plans for themselves. In some areas of health care, records are held by the service user rather than by the service. Antenatal records, infant care records, home dialysis records and diabetes records are commonly held by the service user. Experiments have been made in other circumstances. Gilhooly and McGhee (1991) summarised the research on patient-held records up to 1991 and Christine Hogg evaluated this in 1994, resulting in Table 3.

Table 3   An evaluation of patient-held records

Against patient-held records	*For patient-held records*
Patients will lose their records	Research shows that records are less likely to be lost if held by patients
GPs will need to spend more time explaining the notes	The benefits of spending more time in explaining outweigh this
The costs of producing and updating double copies, where both are necessary	Not always necessary to keep double copies, or modified form of notes can be provided
GPs will feel restricted and keep another set of private notes – i.e. when patients hold the records GPs won't put the truth in them	A study found that GPs were more likely to 'censor' diagnoses such as obesity than cancer or a terminal illness!
Detailed information makes people more anxious	Studies show that access and possession of records reassures patients
Detailed information destroys the rapport and trust between doctor and patient	Studies show that patient-held records increase the rapport between GP and patient
Records kept at home may be seen by other people without permission of the patient	Patients can control the confidentiality of their own records
	Patients can correct any inaccuracies in their records. Studies show 10–12% errors in patients' notes
	Locums and deputies have access to notes on home visits
	Notes can cover both health and social care and improve co-ordination of services
	No delays when patients move or change GPs
	Savings in storage and retrieval in GP surgery

(Source: adapted from Hogg, 1994, diagram 4, p. 47 (7))

In Table 3 Hogg makes a very good case for patient-held records, and by implication for client-held records in social care.

Client-held records have sometimes been used successfully to solve the information problems associated with transient and, particularly, homeless people who move from place to place frequently: people like Jim and Marianne of Unit 10, for example. If such people's records travel with them, then, provided that they are not lost, they are always available when needed.

Giving transient clients their own records to keep is one way of solving the problem of people becoming detached from the service records concerning them. But modern information technology suggests other ways. Fax already allows for more rapid transfer of information from one authority to another, so that records can chase people round the country more quickly.

Electronic patient records (EPRs) are technically feasible (Silicon Bridge Research, 1997). EPRs are not simply records typed into a computer, but records which can be read by the computer so that, on instruction, the computer can search for names, conditions, medications, or kinds of care packages, and can produce summaries, and so on. There are many hospitals in the USA and in continental Europe, and several in the UK (Cross, 1997a) where all patient records made in the hospital are in electronic form. In the UK there are specialist networks for ordering tests and transmitting test results from laboratories to GP or hospital, and a national network for finding beds in hospitals. However, there is no network for transmitting electronic patient and other information throughout the NHS, still less between the NHS and other agencies. Rather, information is printed out from one computer and then typed or scanned into another. The solution to the problem is to persuade all the NHS trusts, health authorities and GPs to subscribe to the same HISS (Health Information Support System) (Cross, 1997b, 1997c). In 1997 an authoritative source estimated that it would be 2007 before there was a complete system for transmitting records electronically throughout the NHS (Feldbaum and Dick, 1997).

Opening the 1997 Healthcare Computing exhibition, Peter Cochrane of British Telecom demonstrated a tiny 'dog tag' containing a microchip, capable of storing a person's entire lifetime medical records and much more besides (Cross, 1997c). This device, or a smart card, would make it much easier for service users to hold their own records. Microchip implants into the patient's body would make it much less likely that people would lose their records. Unlike paper records which service users hold currently, these electronic records could be serviced over the telephone to keep them up to date, by adding the results of diagnostic

Modern information technology allows for large amounts of personal information to be stored in tiny microchips which might be worn as pendants or bracelets, or incorporated into a smart card

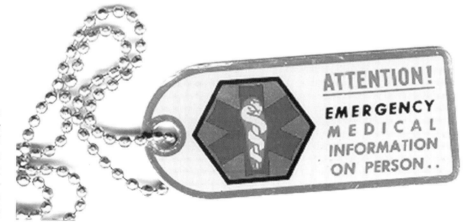

tests for example. They might be read by the patient through a domestic television set with minor adaptations, through a personal computer or, failing that, through a visit to a surgery or some other agency. There is, of course, no reason why patients should not also have printouts of what is stored on their personal microchip.

However, this kind of technology and EPRs have implications for privacy and confidentiality. Once information about a patient is part of a widespread electronic network, there are thousands of different points at which the information can be accessed, legally or illegally – unlike the limited opportunities for this with paper records (Feldbaum and Dick, 1997).

One of the advantages of service users having easy access to their own records, perhaps through holding them themselves, is that this makes it much easier for them to check for errors. All research on health and social care records, paper-based or electronic, shows that they are riddled with errors. A common finding for GP records is that around 12 per cent contain inaccuracies (Gilhooly and McGhee, 1991), while studies of social work records suggest that anything up to 24 per cent contain errors (Barnes, 1993). These are minimal figures since those who research the accuracy of records can usually check only the most elementary kinds of facts, such as names, dates of birth, dates of treatments, addresses, and so on. Such research can rarely check whether a diagnosis was correct, or correctly recorded, or whether a social worker's interpretation of a family's problem was accurate or a service user's wishes were faithfully recorded. Some simple errors might have grave consequences, and it is not unknown for records relating to one person to be added to the files of another, or for misspellings of names or errors in file numbers to result in two parallel sets of information being maintained for the same person, neither of which contains the complete story. In hospitals it is common for between 10 and 15 per cent of (paper-based) records to be missing when required (Audit Commission, 1995b), and in this sense these records might be regarded as 100 per cent wrong.

One of the unexpected side effects of computerisation seems to be that practitioners now have less faith in the accuracy of records, believing in the GIGO principle, 'garbage in, garbage out' (Glastonbury, 1995; Willis, 1997). There is no evidence that computer-based records are any more inaccurate than paper-based ones, but a healthy scepticism about accuracy in records seems in order, at least to the extent that practitioners make attempts to verify records rather than treating them as gospel truth. Service users are sometimes themselves the source of errors in records, as you will see below.

2.5 Records made by service users

Service users and informal carers supply workers with a great deal of information, edited versions of which subsequently appear in the records. Renal (kidney failure) patients may be asked to keep a record of their food and fluid intake. Parents may be asked to complete records of a child's progress on a programme designed to remedy bed-wetting. In the same kind of programme the child may be involved in recording by sticking stars on his or her own continence chart. Depression management programmes and programmes for dealing with panic attacks often entail diaries kept by the client and self-assessment forms filled in by the client periodically (see the example opposite). Applications for most welfare benefits are records which are usually filled in by applicants themselves. So also are 'customer satisfaction' questionnaires and complaints forms.

Diary Sheet

Please make an entry whenever you notice a definite increase in anxiety

Date/time	Description of situation	Anxiety level: 0–10	Description of (a) physical feelings (b) thoughts	Coping method	Anxiety level after: 0–10

20

A diary of anxiety levels. Sometimes service users are the best people to make records about themselves. This may be when the information is about their feelings, which they know best about, or when they are out of contact with practitioners. Making a record yourself helps you learn about yourself

Conditions for service users to make records

Involving service users in making their own records assumes that they have the necessary expertise to do so. Currently, some of those most likely to hold and make entries into their own records include patients and carers who preside over home dialysis, and people with diabetes who manage their own medication and who test and record their own blood sugar levels. Both these groups have to receive training to manage their own care and to record it appropriately. They are, as it were, transformed from patients to workers even if they are unpaid for the work they do. Greater involvement in record making teaches clients skills they can use in self-assertion and self-care but it may also require training so that they know how to recognise what is relevant and recordable.

Involving service users and their carers in making records is transferring to them some of the tasks more usually done by paid workers. For this to be successful it is necessary for them to show the same characteristics as are expected of paid workers.

While most users of services might be expected to be honest and punctilious in making their own records, there are those who are not. In renal units, where people come for kidney dialysis, a major problem is the untrustworthiness of patients when making records of their diet and fluid intakes between dialysis sessions. They often eat and drink a great deal more than they admit to. It is difficult for clinicians to make judgements about treatment when they cannot be certain if patients are telling the truth. It also prevents good relationships being formed between staff and patients. Nurses in most renal units are supposed to engage in counselling relationships with patients. In counselling relationships the counsellor is supposed to adopt a 'non-judgemental' approach to the service user, which means not showing that they disapprove of their behaviour (Inskipp, 1988). Nurses find this very difficult when faced with patients who are obviously lying to them in presenting their self-completed dietary records. Even if nurses are able to be non-judgemental, the relationships they are able to make with the patients are somewhat soured by some patients knowing that they are involved in systematic untruth, and other patients knowing that they are likely to be regarded with suspicion also. Patients also have suspicions, not entirely unfounded, that those who stick to their diets and fluid regimes are those who will be selected for transplants or home dialysis. They have some very good reasons for lying (Gomm, 1989).

Activity 8   **Untrustworthy recorders**

Allow about 10 minutes   Think about the problem in renal units described above. Is there a case for not asking patients to maintain records of their diet and fluid intake between visits to the renal unit? What do you think?

Comment   Here's one possible response. *If this can be done safely*, it is better to treat patients as trustworthy even if they might not be, rather than treat them as untrustworthy even if they are worthy of trust. The safety issue in this case cannot be managed by finding another way of recording diet and fluid intake between visits to the unit. At home, what patients eat and drink has to be recorded by someone there. Nurses wish from time to time that relatives could do the recording, but recognise that this would infantilise the patients and discourage them from taking responsibility for themselves (Gomm, 1989). The backstop for safety is the weighing and other examinations done before patients are put on the dialysis machines. Given these safety measures, the risk of patients falsifying their record sheets is worth taking in an attempt to get them to take more responsibility for their own care.

Under other circumstances, considerations of safety might lead practitioners to the opposite conclusion. For example, in prescribing methadone and other drugs for heroin addiction doctors will ask the patient about their recent drug-taking behaviour. But they usually regard the answers with some scepticism and resort to a urine test. The reason for this is that safe prescribing for people addicted to opiates requires precise information about recent drug-taking behaviour. Prescribing on the basis of self-recording (or self-reports) is just too risky for most doctors to contemplate (Waller, 1993). Unfortunately, doctors have a good basis in fact for being suspicious of what people like Marianne and Jim tell them.

Both the examples above involve the same kind of calculation. How far do the risks of believing service users outweigh the benefits of treating them as believable? This is not just an issue about allowing service users to make their own records. It is also an issue where practitioners have to decide on the truth of what clients or patients tell them and whether to write this into the records themselves. You might like to think about this in relation to the following examples: believing diabetic patients' estimates of their sugar consumption; believing offenders' accounts that they have been law-abiding between meetings with their probation officer or supervising social worker; believing the account of a man suspected of sexually abusing his stepchildren.

However, sometimes it doesn't really matter whether what the service user says or writes is accurate or true. For example, in reminiscence work (Unit 16) it may be that nothing hinges on the truth of what service users say. Indeed, one school of thought associated with reminiscence – validation therapy – instructs practitioners to treat as true whatever the service user says, however incredible (Feil, 1992).

It is important to remember that not all clients wanting to use services would be happy about assessing their own needs and making their own plans, participating in their own treatments and recording all this, even if someone helped them with the recording. And some people are too ill or confused to do this.

Key points

- Whenever the question has been researched, records held by service users have proved less likely to be lost than service-held records.

- Whenever they have been researched, health and social care records have been found to be riddled with errors. This is less often the case when service users hold their own records, or are given opportunities to check them for accuracy.

- Modern information technology promises electronic records which can be speedily transmitted from place to place and quickly updated. The problem of co-ordination discussed in Unit 18 has slowed the implementation of modern IT systems such as EPRs (Electronic Patient Records).

- When service users are allowed to make entries into their own records this may give them an opportunity to record what they think is important to them, and it includes them as 'partners in care'.

- Service users and informal carers may need some training if they are to be involved in making entries into the records of health and social care, but this will enhance their ability to make decisions for themselves and care for themselves.

- There are limits of capability, expertise and trustworthiness, and considerations of safety which may put limits on how far service users can contribute to their own records. These limits do not apply when, as in reminiscence work, nothing hinges on the truth or falsity of the records.

Section 3
Privacy and confidentiality

The previous section considered the issue of service users making their own entries into records, and the arguments in favour of this. This section is about the opposite concern. It is about how service users might keep information about themselves off the record, and how they might determine how recorded information about themselves is shared and used.

3.1 Choice in disclosure

The most obvious way in which the users of services can control information about themselves is to refuse to disclose it. But do would-be users of services have a real choice about this?

A simple way of answering this question is to say that whatever service it is, there will be a minimum amount of information which the client has to disclose *as a condition* for receiving the service. Thus the doctor might say to the patient, 'Unless you drop your trousers I can't do any more about the pain in your groin.' The counsellor might say to the client, 'I respect your right to privacy but if you are not going to disclose your feelings to me, then it's not worth us continuing this counselling relationship.' The Benefits Agency official might say to the claimant, 'Unless you can provide me with evidence that you are not engaged in paid work I can't go on authorising your income support.' In this sense clients may have a choice, but it is the choice between disclosing and receiving the service, and not disclosing and not receiving the service.

Many service users find practitioners' questions offensive. This raises the question of whether practitioners need to ask certain questions, and if they ask them whether they should record the answers.

Activity 9   **Intrusion or the need to know**

Allow about 15 minutes   For this activity read the following text, 'Assessment queries "offensive" says client'. You will see that the service user, Deanna Egan, took offence at being asked for two kinds of information: about her abilities in personal care, and about her own and her partner's financial situation. Consider (a) whether the social services department needed to know this information, and (b) if they did need to know it whether they needed to record it.

> **Assessment queries 'offensive' says client**
>
> A blind and physically disabled woman has complained to her council after being shocked by 'insulting and personal' questions used in her reassessment at a rehabilitation day centre.
>
> Faced with questions on menstruation, her ability to get into and out of bed, on and off the toilet and take a shower, Deanna Egan refused to be reassessed for her place at the council-run centre in Norwood, south London, which she has used twice a week for about six years.

'They are very offensive. I don't think a day centre needs to know all this. I was told if I didn't sign the form I would lose my place at the centre', she said.

But this was denied by a spokesperson for the London Borough of Lambeth, who said no one would lose their place for refusing a reassessment.

[...]

But as far as Egan is concerned, the centre only needed to know her disability, her GP's name and the name of her partner or carer.

'It should be up to each user to raise any personal issues verbally. It should not be written down so that anyone can see it', she said.

[...]

Egan was also astounded to see a section in the form requesting information on her own and her partner's income.

[...]

A council spokesperson maintained that these questions were necessary to assess the level of personal hygiene care required and because 'people's care needs may change over time'.

Financial questions were necessary 'in case we should decide to implement a charging policy'.

(Valios, 1996, p. 9)

Comment   (a)   Need to know

Abilities in personal care. Given that this is a rehabilitation centre whose task is to help users to improve their daily living skills, it does seem important that staff know what users can do, and how much their abilities change over time. Asking service users for their views on this seems rather better than staff recording such matters without asking.

Financial situation. Given that central government allocates finances to social services departments on the assumption that they will raise income from charging for services such as this, and that charges should be levied according to ability to pay, it does seem as if the council needs to have this information if it is likely to levy charges in the future.

(b)   Need to record

Abilities in personal care. If providing a service were just a matter between a worker and a service user then perhaps there would be no need to record this information. But recording allows for continuity of care. Moreover, this is a publicly funded service, so it has to be accountable for providing appropriate services to people who have a need for them and benefit from them. It is difficult to see how it could be accountable without recording service users' abilities and progress.

Financial situation. The only way in which a social services department can demonstrate that it is levying charges according to its own scheme of charging is to make records of the financial circumstances of the service users and of the fees they are charged.

From the article it is not clear exactly what questions were asked, and how offensive their phrasing was, or the manner in which they were asked and how insulting that was. But so long as you accept that the task of this day centre is to facilitate the development of daily living skills, then you have to accept that staff need to know what skills the centre users have. How could staff do their jobs otherwise? You might object to charges being made, but if they are to be made, then asking questions about income seems inevitable. Perhaps the most important point, however, is that publicly funded services are not private matters between a service user and a service. It is not like using a private gym for which the users pay themselves. These are public services and have to be publicly accountable, although usually in ways that protect the identity of the service users concerned. It is quite legitimate for any member of the public, a local authority councillor, an auditor, or the Social Services Inspectorate to ask of the local authority, 'Are you spending public money in ways that help those people who have a right to be helped?', or 'Are you charging for services in a way that is fair?' Without asking the kind of questions asked of Deanna Egan and recording the answers, the local authority would not be able to answer such questions itself.

On the issue of personal living skills, centre staff probably made records even though Deanna Egan didn't answer the questions herself, and probably less accurately that she would have done. On the issue of finance Deanna Egan has a choice. If she doesn't disclose her financial situation and Lambeth levies charges, she will be billed at the highest rate. There is some evidence that some service users choose not to use services rather than disclose their financial circumstances (Dobson, 1996).

An additional part of Deanna Egan's complaint, not included above, was that:

> *If the council had to pass the financial part of the form to a relevant department the personal information would accompany it.*
>
> *(Valios, 1996, p. 9)*

If this was indeed the case, it would be a shocking breach of confidentiality. But there is no reason why all the information collected about a particular service user should travel together. Well-designed systems of record keeping stratify information so that different portions can be transmitted to different people on a need-to-know basis. In fact, much of the information which is used for monitoring purposes (function 4 in Table 1) is anonymised. For example, agencies catering for people with drug problems complete quarterly returns to the regional drug database. The agency keeps the part of the form which identifies the drug user and what goes to the regional drug database consists only of anonymous information.

Sometimes service users have virtually no choice but to disclose information. For example, pre-sentence reports (PSRs) are completed by probation officers to aid the court in deciding an appropriate sentence.

The offender can refuse to co-operate in this, but in doing so would be passing over an opportunity to influence the sentence.

By contrast there are some services which require very little disclosure from their clients at all. These include the services of the Samaritans (which are available to people who remain anonymous), night shelters and other facilities for the homeless, and the services of needle and syringe exchanges which routinely and knowingly deal with people who give false names for the records such exchanges have to keep.

Key point

- For any health or social care service there will be a minimum of information which clients are required to disclose as a condition for receiving the service. In this sense a would-be service user has no real choice about disclosure.

3.2 Confidentiality and consent

Health and social care work records are rarely just made as an *aide-mémoire* for the person who makes them. Although some counsellors and psychotherapists in private practice keep records which are privy to themselves and the client concerned, most records in health and care are made with a view to the information in them being shared. On the one hand, this is so that continuity of care is not vulnerable to individual practitioners becoming sick, going on holiday or changing their jobs. Records allow successors, colleagues and locums to pick up where another left off. On the other hand, health and social care is often provided for the same person by diverse practitioners in diverse agencies, who all need to share some of the same information, and who all need to know what each other is up to. Records are an important facility for co-ordinating care. Sharing the information in records raises issues about whom the information should be shared with, what they may or may not do with it, and what rights clients have to know how and with whom information about themselves is likely to be shared.

Whether they realise it or not, when patients tell something to a doctor they are authorising the sharing of that information with colleagues and secretaries, records clerks and managers in the same agency, and perhaps with a range of people in other agencies as well.

Implicit consent

The NHS operates the rather paradoxical doctrine of *implicit consent*. This is paradoxical because it is a way of giving consent without giving consent. Unless patients specifically ask otherwise, they are deemed to have consented to the information they have given to one practitioner in the service being shared with others. The English Department of Health's version of the doctrine of implicit consent is shown in the next box. You will see that it applies not only to the transfer of information, but also to the administration of treatment.

The doctrine of implicit consent

Unless they specifically state otherwise it is assumed that service users have given 'implicit consent' to:

- the transfer of information given to one practitioner within the NHS to other practitioners involved in the patient's care

- the transfer of information held within the NHS to social services involved in the patient's care.

A patient who is unable to give informed consent is deemed to have given implicit consent to actions which are performed in his or her own interests.

The doctrine of implicit consent should not be over-used. It is good practice to ask for explicit consent.

When acting on 'implicit consent' practitioners have a duty of care to ensure that information is only shared with those who:

- have a legitimate right to know

- can be trusted to act in the patient's interests or, failing that, the public interest

- can be trusted not to disclose the information improperly.

Implicit consent applies to consent to treatment, to transfer of care from one health and social care agency to another as well as consent to the transfer of information.

(Adapted from Department of Health, 1996c, OHT29)

From this box you will see that there are some very good reasons why the doctrine of implicit consent is necessary. It refers to 'a patient who is unable to give informed consent'. This includes people who are unconscious, or very agitated or confused. It would obviously be impossible to run health and social services if no information could be transferred before an unconscious patient regained consciousness, or unless a person with Alzheimer's disease became lucid enough to be asked permission. In strictly legal terms the extent to which an adult person's 'next of kin' can give consent to the transfer of information about their relative is a rather cloudy area, but the idea of implicit consent makes seeking such permission unnecessary. In addition, however capable the person might be, it would make health services very difficult to run if consent was required for each and every occasion that records passed from person to person: hospital doctors, social workers, medical students, general practitioners, medical records officers, chaplains, secretaries, ward clerks, radiographers, pharmacists, practice managers, locums, agency staff, and so on.

However, as it says in the box, it is considered good practice to ask for explicit consent whenever this is possible:

> *3.1   All NHS bodies must have an active policy for informing patients of the kind of purposes for which information about them is collected and categories of people or organisations to which information may need to be passed.*
>
> *(Department of Health, 1996a, p. 7)*

Explicit consent

Although social services and social work departments and other agencies in the health and social field often seem to behave as if they had policies of implicit consent, in fact they do not. Hence the well-run agency will seek explicit consent for information about service users to be shared within the agency concerned, and perhaps more widely, as the example shows.

Other Agencies Involved	Contact Name	Tel. No.	Date

CLIENT INFORMATION SHARING AGREEMENT

I agree that the details contained in this assessment can be shared with other agencies involved in my care.

Client/Patient signature

Date

Some social services departments make it clear to service users that information about them will be shared within the agency and sometimes beyond. This example is based on forms used by Kent County Council

The idea of explicit consent implies that the person gives consent, knowing exactly what they are agreeing to – informed explicit consent. This suggests that agencies should take care to explain the implications of divulging information to the person who is asked for it. As with other kinds of communication discussed earlier, this explanation needs to be in terms understandable to service users, answering the questions they need answered. Overleaf is an example of an attempt to explain the confidentiality of the national registration of drug addicts using a cartoon strip format. Since this cartoon was drawn, the practice of registering drug addicts with the Home Office has been discontinued as serving no useful purpose and as too expensive and too intrusive of privacy.

It is not always possible to predict in advance how information obtained confidentially might be used in the future. Some medical records, such as those for midwifery and obstetrics, have by law to be kept for 25 years (Department of Health, 1996a, 4.13). The civil liberties climate in Britain could change quite radically in a quarter of a century, overturning previous commitments to keep information confidential. Although there would have been no commitment to keep the records of the inmates of Lennox Castle confidential, few of them in the 1930s or '40s would have predicted that their personal case notes would be available in the public archives in the 1990s.

Earlier in this unit it was suggested that it is important to keep the recording of information to the minimum necessary. The reason given then was in terms of the costs of collecting and curating information. But considerations of confidentiality lead to the same conclusion. The difficulty, as always, is deciding what is the minimum necessary.

Leaflet published by Lifeline, Manchester

3.3 Enforcing confidentiality

The devices used in attempting to enforce confidentiality include the following.

- Agency confidentiality policies – you will look at one of these in Unit 21 and try applying it in practice.

- Contracts of employment in which failure to follow the agency confidentiality policy can be a dismissible offence.

- Complaints procedures which allow clients who feel that their confidentiality has been breached to complain about the person concerned (e.g. Department of Health, 1995c; National Health Service Executive, 1996a).

- Professional codes of conduct. Those practitioners who are members of professional associations, such as doctors, nurses, chiropodists or occupational therapists, are bound by codes of conduct which always include clauses on maintaining confidentiality and not taking advantage of confidential information. Breaching such codes can lead to disciplinary action by the professional association, and might lead to the person being struck from the professional register and hence being unable to continue to practise (e.g. General Medical Council, 1993; United Kingdom Central Council for Nursing, Midwifery and Health Visiting, 1993).

- Laws requiring organisations to protect confidential information. The most important of these is the Data Protection Act 1984, which in October 1998 will be joined by the 1995 European Directive on Data Protection. Details about this legislation are shown in the next box.

- The civil law gives people who believe their confidentiality has been breached the opportunity to sue for damages – but only if they can demonstrate that some tangible harm has come to them in consequence.

- International treaty obligations, such as the European Convention on Human Rights, also guarantee privacy and confidentiality. You will be looking at this in Section 4.

The Data Protection Act 1984 and the 1995 European Directive on Data Protection

The Data Protection Act covers only computerised records, although it is regarded as good practice to apply the same principles to paper-based records. It applies to records about people where what is recorded is not a matter of public knowledge. The agency has to register with the Data Protection Registrar, becoming thereby accountable to the registrar for making sure that the information recorded:

- was obtained legally and without deceit

- is used only for the purpose for which it was collected, which must be the purpose explained to the person from whom it was collected

- is relevant to the purpose for collecting it and contains no more than is necessary

- was accurate when collected and, where necessary, is kept up to date

- should be kept no longer than is necessary

and that:

- appropriate security measures are taken to prevent unauthorised access

- individuals are entitled to see the data held about them and should know their entitlement.

The main effects of the European Directive will be to extend this code to paper-based records and to lift restrictions on personal access to records made before certain dates (for example the 1991 threshold for health records). At the time of writing, however, the exact details of its incorporation into British law are undecided.

(Adapted from Data Protection Registrar, 1994; Home Office, 1996a)

As noted in Unit 18, health authorities and social services or social work departments have used their purchaser power to enforce confidentiality policies on independent providers. Although some voluntary sector agencies have always maintained stricter codes of confidentiality than the statutory services, others have been very lax in this regard (Knight, 1993). Confidentiality, with regard to gossip or records, can be particularly difficult to maintain in agencies with informal styles of working and where 'workers' may be volunteers, or service users themselves, without the contracts of employment or memberships of professional associations which can be used to discipline paid workers. One approach to this is to avoid recording personal details almost entirely (as the mental health charity MIND advises: Villeneau, 1994). But when voluntary organisations take on contracts, this usually involves them in recording information about service users (National Health Service Executive, 1995).

Despite all the attempts to maintain confidentiality, anyone who works in the NHS or in a local authority social services or social work department will know that they are rather 'leaky' so far as confidentiality is concerned. Many people who work there simply do discuss patients or clients with their spouses and their friends, even if they usually try to do so without identifying them. However, such breaches of confidentiality do not usually concern what is written into the records. More usually the breaches come from the tittle-tattle of working life. By comparison with gossip, the confidentiality of records is relatively easy to ensure. Because records are physical objects they can be locked away, or, if electronic, can be protected with passwords and security codes or by encryption. In the last resort it is impossible to defeat a determined hacker, but it is possible to make unauthorised access difficult (Feldbaum and Dick, 1997).

Activity 10   **How much harm does it do?**

Allow about 10 minutes   At first sight it may not seem to be too serious a matter if someone's private affairs become known by outsiders to the health and care services, particularly if they don't know that they are being talked about behind their back. Perhaps you would like to think about this. Jot down some ideas about when such a breach of confidentiality might be seriously harmful to someone.

Comment   Once information is outside the group of people who are bound by a confidentiality policy there is no knowing where it might get to, or how distorted it might become in the retelling. Some kinds of information can be very discrediting, for example information that someone has had a test for HIV or has attended a clinic for sexually transmitted diseases, has had an appointment with a psychiatrist, or has attended Alcoholics Anonymous. If that person's partner doesn't know and gets to hear about it on the grapevine, it won't bode well for their relationship. If a current or prospective employer gets to know, it might ruin someone's job prospects. Sometimes confidential records contain information about illegitimate children that a person wants kept confidential from a current partner, or past criminal offences, or information that they were themselves adopted, or that they had a sex change operation, that they are gay, and so on and so on. Some confidential information has a commercial value. Examples include medical information, information from genetic testing which is of interest to insurance companies and any information about celebrities which will be of interest to the media. And of course, there is always the possibility of blackmail.

Key points

- Best practice is always to make efforts to explain to service users what information collected about them will be used for, and with whom it is likely to be shared.

- This puts them in a position to give explicit and informed consent or to decide against providing the information.

- Sometimes, however, the service user may not be in a position to consent. Then decisions have to be taken by others with the service user's best interests in mind.

- There is a large array of devices for enforcing confidentiality via agency codes, employment contracts, professional codes of practice and parliamentary and EU legislation.

- Nonetheless, health and social care agencies are often 'leaky', particularly with regard to gossip rather than to records.

Study skills: Keeping your K100 filing system in shape

With all this talk about records and their uses, what do *you* actually do with your own written records of your studies (your notes and TMAs)? Can you find your way to what you need – or has your course work become just a big pile? Every student needs an effective filing system. In many ways your filing system is more important than your memory. Nobody remembers everything, but clever students can find their way to *what* they need to know *when* they need to know it. However, filing isn't easy. A complicated system can be self-defeating, too time-consuming and too hard to remember. You need something fairly simple and also flexible (so that you aren't left with lots of pieces of paper which don't fit anywhere). But when you start working in a new area, you can't easily tell what shape of filing system is going to work well. Generally it's best to start with a very obvious and simple system and then modify it as you go along.

Have you modified any of your K100 files? What labels do you currently have on your folders? When did you last bring your files up to date? Is it time to do some reorganising and relabelling? (A supply of sticky labels can be very useful. If your files are easy to relabel, you are more likely to get round to doing it.)

It isn't *just* a matter of ensuring quick access to information. Organising your files is a way of making yourself think about how the course is organised. By the time you have worked out an effective filing system for your course notes, you have learned something pretty fundamental about the nature and content of the course.

Section 4

Confidentiality, co-ordination and the public interest

There are situations in which the argument for disclosing confidential information is more persuasive than the argument for keeping it confidential. This section considers such situations.

4.1 Overriding rights to confidentiality

Like all rights, the rights to privacy and confidentiality are conditional. People have such rights only if they satisfy certain conditions. This is quite clear in the major body of law guaranteeing civil rights in Britain: the European Convention on Human Rights. Britain is already a signatory to this convention but before the millennium it will be incorporated fully into British law. This means that British citizens will more often be able to have matters of civil rights settled in the British courts, and less often need to go to the European Court of Human Rights for this purpose.

The Convention covers both privacy and confidentiality in Article 8. This says:

> *Article 8*
>
> 1 *Everyone has the right to respect for his/her private and family life, his/her home and correspondence.*
>
> 2 *There shall be no interference by a public authority with the exercise of this right except in accordance with the law and as is necessary in a democratic society in the interests of national security, public safety, or the economic well being of the country, for the prevention of disorder or crime, or the protection of health or morals, or for the assertion of the rights and freedoms of others.*
>
> *(European Convention on Human Rights Article 8, in Brownlie, 1983, p. 246)*

In this statement a lot seems to depend on who defines what is 'necessary', what is 'disorder', what is 'moral', and so on. But this is not entirely a matter for the government concerned. On several occasions in the 1980s and '90s the European Court of Human Rights overruled the British Government's definition of such terms. On the whole the European Court is most interested in striking a balance between one individual's right to privacy and the benefits to others of the information not remaining private.

Activity 11   **Exceptions to the right to privacy and confidentiality**

Allow about 10 minutes   Look again at the quotation from Article 8 of the European Convention on Human Rights. You will see that it first grants 'everyone' these rights, and then allows some people's rights to privacy and confidentiality to be overridden by other considerations. For this activity jot down a list of the kinds of people or activities you think *should not* be covered by a right of privacy/confidentiality.

Comment   In response to this question most people list a wide range of criminal activities, such as child abuse, drug dealing, money laundering, terrorism, and so on. Some suggest a formula such as 'there should be no right to keep private those activities which harm other people'.

It was in this spirit that the government established a register of sexual offenders under the Sexual Offences Act 1997 (Home Office, 1996b) and supervision registers (in England) for people with mental illness diagnoses regarded as dangerous to others (Department of Health, 1995a). You are probably aware of the positive vetting of criminal records which is practised before people can be employed to work with vulnerable service users.

The same formula could be applied as a justification for overriding an organisation's attempts to keep safety hazards or unsafe levels of staffing a secret by including 'gagging' clauses in the contracts of employees.

Some people also consider that a person should not have a right to privacy or confidentiality of information if this right means that harm will come to them. They would like to see a formula such as: 'there should be no right for a person to keep private those activities which will harm him- or herself'.

As this activity suggests, codes of confidentiality usually have exclusions for people who have committed certain kinds of criminal offences and/or may be a danger to themselves and others. In fact, the law regarding confidentiality and privacy with regard to people who are merely a risk to themselves is extremely complicated and somewhat contradictory. In brief, the situation is that if an adult is put at risk by their own desire for confidentiality, then that is their affair, unless they can be regarded as mentally incapacitated and hence unfit to make this decision. In that case their rights to confidentiality can be legally breached (Law Society/British Medical Association, 1995).

The situation where someone is harming themselves and wishes to keep this confidential is frequently confronted by the volunteers who work for the Samaritans, the telephone helpline for people who are desperate and suicidal.

> *You do just have to listen, sometimes for hours while the person is dying of an overdose or bleeding to death at the end of the 'phone, and knowing that if you dialled 1471, you could probably trace the call, and alert the emergency services and save their life. But if the person doesn't want that then that's their right. That's how Sams do it.*
>
> *(Samaritan volunteer)*

Committing suicide ceased to be a criminal offence in 1961. Since in Britain there is no legal duty under the criminal law for citizens to prevent crime, there would be no legal obligation to report the likelihood of suicide even if it were still illegal. On the other hand, someone who wants to commit suicide seems to have no legal right to have that kept secret either. Samaritans will not breach confidentiality because of their operational policy, but there is no legal reason why someone else should not. The operational policies of prisons and hospitals make it a requirement for staff to report on the suicidal intentions of inmates. All this is just an aspect of a more general legal confusion about how far people have the right to harm themselves intentionally, and how far others have an obligation to prevent them doing so.

Matters are rather clearer with regard to confidentiality and people who are engaged in criminal activity, or who might harm others. Many practitioners in health and social care get to know information relevant to criminal offences, particularly those committed in a domestic context such as sexual or physical abuse, and information about illegal immigration, illicit drug use, benefit fraud, various kinds of 'under-age' offences: drinking, driving and sexual behaviour. Much of this information they discover under circumstances of confidentiality. There are no legal penalties for failing to report this information and in practice many practitioners do not volunteer such information to the police or immigration authorities, unless someone else's safety is at risk. Most practitioners do render up information when, and only when, this is required by a warrant or a court order, or when they are subpoenaed to appear as witnesses in court. Thus the usual confidentiality of medical or social work records can be overridden by the courts. Rather fewer practitioners refuse to breach confidentiality when required to do so by the courts, as they would risk being fined or imprisoned for contempt of court.

As you might have guessed from Section 3.3, people who work in health and social care are usually regarded by the civil courts as having a 'duty of confidentiality'. This makes it legal for employers to dismiss them for breaching confidentiality and allows service users to sue them (or their agencies) for damages if confidentiality is breached. However, the courts may also regard people who work in health and social care as having a duty to warn and a duty to protect (Rapaport, 1996) when the safety of a third party is involved. The case usually cited in this respect is the Tarasoff case (Stone, 1984). Here a psychotherapist, knowing that his client had an intention to kill someone, failed to disclose this. The killing took place and the psychotherapist was successfully sued by the victim's relatives. Thus the civil law lays contradictory duties on people who work in health and social care.

Most agencies and most professional groups have policies or codes of practice to aid them in making decisions in particular cases, and these differ. But a general consideration is always this question, 'Will more harm be done by maintaining confidentiality than by breaching it?'

This is often a question which is difficult to answer, partly because it involves predicting the future, and partly because giving a benefit to one person may be doing harm to another. Dilemmas of this kind can be especially acute where no criminal act has been committed, yet the client's behaviour constitutes a risk to someone else, and the information has been obtained in confidence.

Activity 12   **Should we tell the partner?**

Allow about 10 minutes   Imagine you are a worker in a drug agency. Currently, the agency has a strict policy of confidentiality, which will only be breached in cases of harm to the welfare of children, rape, and serious physical injury due to violent assault. This is written in large letters on the wall of the agency and all clients are told this when they first make contact. During your dealings with a client you learn that he is HIV positive, that he is having unprotected sex with his partner and sharing needles with her. She does not know his HIV status, and she is also a client of the agency.

(a)   What do you think you should do given the existing confidentiality policy?

(b)   Do you think the policy needs to be changed?

Comment

There is a possibility that knowingly infecting someone with HIV may be made a criminal offence, in which case agencies would have to reconsider their confidentiality policies.

(a) It would be an act of extreme bad faith to depart from a policy so explicitly stated. Perhaps this is the reason why some agencies make no, or only vague, commitments to their clients about confidentiality – but that doesn't seem like good practice either. In more practical terms agencies which renege on their commitments are very likely to lose the trust not only of the client concerned, but of all those clients the aggrieved one talks to. Probably the best you can do in these circumstances is to try to persuade the client to give you permission to tell his partner, or to persuade him to tell her himself. It's probably too late to protect his partner by starting to use safer sex methods or give up sharing needles, but this should have been the advice given whatever the situation.

(b) What makes this such a difficult case is that this agency has a duty of care to two clients, and has a policy which promises them confidentiality from each other. It is never clear how much responsibility an agency has towards people at risk who are not its clients unless they are children, because child protection legislation makes virtually everyone responsible for the welfare of children. So the case would have been different had only the man who was HIV positive been a client. But here the agency finds itself in a cleft stick, having to balance the interests of two clients. Doesn't the partner have a right to benefit from the information the agency possesses? Isn't it an act of bad faith not to use it ? You may think that the existing policy should be changed. There is a case for that. Or you may feel it ought to stay the same. And there is a case for that too.

Imagine that it is proposed that the drug agency alters its confidentiality policy to include the clause in bold type below:

Everything you tell us will be strictly confidential:
– unless keeping it confidential will harm the welfare of a child
– unless it involves rape or injury from a violent assault
*– **unless we learn that you are HIV positive and are practising unsafe sex with your partner, who is unaware of this. In this case we may let your partner know.***

Adding this clause would empower the agency to reduce risks to the partners of HIV positive people. But of course, including such a clause would make it highly unlikely that clients would tell the agency the truth about their HIV status or their risky behaviour. The clients most likely to disclose this information under the new policy would be those most likely to be persuaded to give permission for disclosure under the old. Thus adding the new clause seems likely to bring few benefits and might discourage some clients from using the agency at all.

This case featured confidentiality and a sexual partner. Some of the most acute confidentiality dilemmas arise where information is kept secret from relatives, partners, friends and informal carers.

4.2 Confidentiality, carers and relatives

In strictly legal terms the adult relatives, partners or friends of an adult service user seem rarely to have any more rights to receive service information about the service user than any other member of the public if the person concerned is capable of making decisions for him- or herself. Relatives and other co-residents only have the same rights as any other member of the public when their own safety is threatened by not disclosing the information to them. Where the service user is deemed incapable of making decisions, legally information may be shared with 'next of kin' or with a legal guardian on a need-to-know basis without consent, unless before becoming incapacitated the service user explicitly requested that this should not be done. In practice, although this is nowhere written down as policy, many services behave as if a client had given 'implicit consent' for some confidential matters to be shared with informal carers or other relatives, even to the extent of disclosing terminal diagnoses to relatives and not to the dying person (Benson and Britten, 1996)!

 With the passage of the Carers (Recognition and Services) Act 1995, matters have become even more complicated for social services and social work departments. This Act entitles carers to a social services assessment of their needs independently of the assessment of the needs of the person being cared for (see Unit 1). Like the person regarded as the client they also have the right to keep their assessment confidential. Thus social workers may find themselves in a situation where they have assessed the needs of a client and have to keep this confidential from the informal carer, and have assessed the needs of the carer and have to keep this confidential from the client. More usually, they may find themselves with the tricky diplomatic task of negotiating exactly what can be told to each, and what should be mentioned when both are present at the same time. You gained a glimpse of that kind of problem in Unit 1, when you read about Arthur and Lynne Durrant, with Rita, Lynne's disability employment worker, caught between them and having to communicate with both of them, although Lynne herself does not seem to be aware of the problem.

There are situations in which confidentiality from relatives becomes a very delicate matter indeed. For example, in cases of suspected child, spouse or elder abuse, the abused person, or some other witness, cannot be assured of confidentiality because if the suspicion is confirmed services cannot legally let the matter remain confidential. In the fields of drug abuse, mental health and learning disabilities, practitioners have, recently at least, tended to take a hard line in asserting the rights of the client to be able to prohibit information about themselves being shared with relatives. In the last two fields this tendency goes with a belief that people with mental health problems and people with learning disabilities have had their autonomy as individuals undermined. Therefore their rights to be independent persons need to be upheld. Issues of confidentiality then become important aspects of conflicts of interest between service users and informal carers. The former often want independence and privacy from their relatives, while the latter often feel that, although they shoulder the main burden of care, services keep them in the dark:

> We take the bulk of the caring and the worry, we are the ones who cope in the night or who drive miles in the hope he will attend his programme ... We are, or feel, totally excluded from your updates on his condition.
>
> (Quoted in Shepherd et al., 1994, p. 50)

All the major research on the carers of people with mental health problems seems to show that carers feel information they need is kept confidential from them (Borthwick, 1993; Shepherd et al., 1994).

Key point

* The aim to involve informal carers as partners in care may sometimes be subverted by the person cared for asserting their rights not to have confidential information disclosed to informal carers.

4.3 Disclosure in the public interest

There is sometimes a conflict between:

- the need to co-ordinate services
- the need to protect the public
- the need to protect the confidentiality of information
- the client's right to determine who shall see records about him or her.

This section considers this conflict by looking at a very well-known case which exemplifies the difficulties of co-ordinating care at the same time as keeping information confidential. This is the case of Christopher Clunis. What happened to him is similar in many respects to many of those other cases where someone with a mental illness diagnosis has killed someone and where this has been subject to an inquiry (Muijen, 1995). Such cases are rare (Royal College of Psychiatrists, 1996) but when they happen result in extensive news coverage and throw the health and social care agencies concerned into disarray.

Christopher Clunis killed Jonathon Zito, a man who was a complete stranger to him. Zito's wife subsequently founded the mental health charity called the Zito Trust. In the inquiry which followed the death (Ritchie *et al.*, 1994) it emerged that Clunis had a long history of contacts with services, moving through various mental hospitals, moving on to and off the case load of various social services departments and between different hostels and supported accommodation. He was also 'known' to the police and had been on probation from time to time. What really marks the case is the way in which he was always getting separated from the records made about him. Thus he suddenly appeared as a 'new case' in a new agency and everything started from scratch, and then perhaps his records caught up with him or perhaps they did not. In these regards this case is a model of how not to co-ordinate community mental health care.

Inefficiencies on the part of various service agencies played an important part as did the inherent difficulties of transferring cases between agencies. But so also did Clunis's tendency to disappear, to refuse to give details about himself and, on one occasion, to change his name.

In addition, it also seems as if deference to Clunis's rights to confidentiality played a part in the tragedy. It didn't take long before whichever service was dealing with him learned that Clunis was liable to violent outbursts and to sexually harassing behaviour. However, there were at least 15 occasions when practitioners who knew this did not pass this information on to another agency which they knew he had contact with. Sometimes this was probably just sloppy practice. But according to witness statements sometimes this was due to the belief that if these facts were known about him he would be treated disadvantageously.

It may have been an important feature of the case that Clunis was black and that practitioners played down how dangerous he was in a misguided application of anti-discriminatory practice (see Unit 12). For example, it was for this reason that a psychiatric social worker said he did 'not want to stigmatise the patient, or label him in any way as violent or difficult' (Ritchie *et al.*, 1994, p. 37). In the opinion of Vernon Harris, who is a black equal opportunities trainer, this kind of under-reaction is just as racist as over-reaction:

'Large gaps' in care of man who killed, inquiry decides

Hospital error freed man for killing spree

Discharged schizophrenics: Attacks raise disturbing questions over social services' support for mentally ill in the community

Murder that followed a cycle of neglect

Psychiatric patient may sue health bodies for £500,000

'My wife was a schizophrenic, but the doctors let her out. They gave her a month's supply of tablets and told her to get on with it. So she went home and drowned my two beautiful sons'

Mental patient freed to kill

Schizophrenic killer given probation

Grandfather, 83, pushed over wall by man being cared for in the community

Social work staff admit errors over killer lodger

Review slams social services over death

Car was 'lethal weapon' for schizophrenic

Although killings by people with mental health problems, and deaths of children at the hands of their parents, are rare, they are very newsworthy. They blight the careers of practitioners and cause considerable disruption to services while inquiries proceed. Nearly all inquiries have found that poor record keeping is an important contributory factor in such disasters

If they see a black man, vicious and out of control, it is not a racist act to say so. Stereotyping is racist, when the example of one black person is used to classify black people as a group. People are individuals and they must be treated as such.

(Harris, 1994, in Thompson, 1995, p. 14)

And Ratna Dutt of the Race Equality Unit of the National Institute for Social Work says:

Over-reaction, under-reaction, or no reaction at all to black people with mental health problems is a major issue to us. Any of those positions are dangerous and discriminate against black people. If because of such misguided judgement a client ends up killing someone, that is not doing the client or society any favours.

(Quoted in Thompson, 1995, p. 14)

The truth about Clunis's dangerousness was especially kept from accommodation providers, and this is entirely understandable. Social workers and similar practitioners very often have to 'market' a service user to a provider of accommodation (and often to GPs too) and it is not surprising that they do so by withholding discrediting information on the grounds of 'client confidentiality'. The result was that Clunis came to hostels and other kinds of accommodation without the staff being forewarned of the risk he posed to them and other residents. Not long after this case a volunteer was killed in a hostel catering for people with mental health problems (Davies *et al.*, 1995).

It may or may not be the case that the unco-ordinated care experienced by Christopher Clunis led to the death of Jonathon Zito. But it was certainly the case that many hostel staff and residents were placed at considerable risk because information about him was withheld from them. So, as it turned out, were members of the public. Commenting on a number of similar cases, Kent (1996) identifies inadequate recording practice as one of a number of important common features.

Close scrutiny of records seems invariably to lead to serious questions about their accuracy, usefulness and accessibility to other relevant professionals. Incomplete care plans, inaccurate factual information and lost or missing records appear constantly in these inquiries.

(Kent, 1996, p. 18)

Key points

- Those who run services are frequently presented with dilemmas in trying to balance the right of individuals to have their affairs kept private with:
  - the need to share private information in order to co-ordinate services
  - the need to protect the interests and safety of others.
- There are elaborate doctrines concerning confidentiality and consent, but these are often difficult to apply to particular cases.

Conclusion

There were four core questions for this unit. The first of these was:

- What functions do records and recording perform in health and care organisations?

Section 1 of the unit suggested seven different functions for recording. These are shown in Table 1. Although they are sometimes difficult to distinguish one from another, they were accountability, authorisation, decision making, monitoring, co-ordination, making practice systematic and learning from experience or making relationships. Different combinations of these functions require different kinds of records in terms of format, content and process of recording.

The second core question was:

- What do the users of services need from records and how can recording best serve their needs?

Section 2 of the unit discussed this question. It suggested that service users and informal carers need to know who is accountable for providing care, in what ways and how they can complain if this is not done. They need to know their rights, their entitlements, and what other people are authorised to do to them. They need to have at least some of the same information as practitioners in order to make their own decisions about health and social care, and in order to give consent which is informed. And they need to know who has promised to do what, so that if the co-ordination of care breaks down they know who to get in touch with. The same section discussed the way in which service users and carers can be involved in the recording process. First, they can be important in checking the accuracy of records. Second, they are sometimes the best people to hold the records. Third, they can often be involved in making the records themselves.

The third core question was:

- How can those about whom information is recorded control the way it is shared?

The best way in which users of services can control the way information is shared is by not providing it in the first place. But, as Section 3 noted, they often don't have much choice about this. Most services require some information to be provided as a condition of service, while other kinds of information are provided under the duress of the criminal justice or the immigration service. The doctrine of implicit consent is often so 'implicit' that service users don't know about it.

Apart from refusing to provide information there is little service users can do to control the way information about them is shared. In this respect they have to rely on the people who work in health and social care services to tell them what their rights are under whichever confidentiality policy is relevant at the time. And they have to trust workers to treat information about them confidentially. Section 3 noted the various devices used in attempts to enforce confidentiality on workers in health and care. If confidentiality were the overriding aim, the best policy for agencies would be to find out as little information as possible, record even less, and share it only in exceptional circumstances. However, as you saw from the first part of this unit, there can be very strong pressures to collect as much information as possible and, as you saw from the case study of Christopher Clunis, there is a strong argument for sharing information widely.

This raises the last of the core questions:

- How can a balance be struck between respecting the privacy of one individual by keeping recorded information confidential, and protecting the interests of others who may have a legitimate need to know this information?

The short answer to this question is, 'often with great difficulty'. There is nothing particularly special here about records and confidentiality. As in many aspects of health and social care the benefits of one individual may well be achieved to the disadvantage of another (Kohner, 1996). Health and social care practice frequently raises moral dilemmas about whether one person's interests should prevail over those of another, particularly concerning the respective interests of 'client' and informal 'carer'. The issues raised by this core question are just one variety of these kinds of moral dilemma. In Unit 21 you will have the opportunity to look at confidentiality again and think more about such dilemmas.

Records are such a ubiquitous aspect of care that you have not finished with them yet. The next unit in this block is about accountability. As you have already seen, what is on the record makes people accountable for what they have or have not done. This includes whether they have made the records they are supposed to make, and whether they have consulted the records they are supposed to consult. So material on records will also be an important feature of the next unit.

References

Association of Community Health Councils for England and Wales (1993) *NHS Complaints Procedures: A Submission to the Complaints Review Committee*, ACHCE&W, London.

Atkinson, D. and Williams, F. (eds) (1990) *Know Me As I Am: An Anthology of Poetry and Art by People with Learning Difficulties*, Hodder & Stoughton, London.

Audit Commission (1995a) *Setting the Records Straight*, HMSO, London.

Audit Commission (1995b) *For Your Information: A Study of Management Information Systems in the Acute Hospital*, HMSO, London.

Barnes, C. (1993) 'Collecting accurate information about child abuse, revisited', in Glastonbury, B. (ed.) *Human Welfare and Technology*, Van Gorcum, Holland.

Benson, T. (1997) 'The message is the medium', *Health Service Journal* 30 January, pp. 4–5.

Benson, J. and Britten, N. (1996) 'Respecting the autonomy of cancer patients when talking with their families: qualitative analysis of semi-structured interviews', *British Medical Journal*, Vol. 313, pp. 729–31.

Borthwick, A. (1993) *Invisible Pain: The Experience of Being a Relative of a Person with Schizophrenia*, National Schizophrenia Fellowship Scotland, Edinburgh.

Brownlie, I. (ed.) (1983) *Basic Documents on Human Rights* (2nd edn), Clarendon, Oxford.

Cross, M. (1997a) 'For the record', *Health Services Journal*, 30 January, pp. 7–8.

Cross, M. (1997b) 'Full steam ahead', *Health Services Journal*, 30 January, p. 10.

Cross, M. (1997c) 'IT's looking good', *Health Services Journal*, 27 March, p. 18.

Data Protection Registrar (1994) *The Guidelines (3rd Series)*, Office of Data Protection Registrar, Wilmslow.

Davies, N., Lingham, R., Prior, C. and Sims, A. (1995) *Report of the Inquiry into the Circumstances Leading to the Death of Jonathon Newby (a volunteer worker) on 9th October 1993 in Oxford*, Oxfordshire Health Authority, Oxford.

Department of Health (1991a) *Care Management and Assessment: Practitioners' Guide*, HMSO, London.

Department of Health (1991b) *The Patient's Charter*, HMSO, London.

Department of Health (1994a) *Inspection of Assessment and Care Management in Social Services Departments October 1993–March 1994*, HMSO, London.

Department of Health (1994b) *Confidentiality: The Use and Disclosure of Personal Health Information*, HMSO, London.

Department of Health (1994c) *A Framework for Community Care Charters in England: Consultative Document*, HMSO, London.

Department of Health (1995a) *Building Bridges: Guide to Arrangements for Inter-agency Working for the Care and Protection of Severely Mentally Ill People*, HMSO, London.

Department of Health (1995b) *The Patient's Charter* (revised edn), HMSO, London.

Department of Health (1995c) *Acting on Complaints*, Department of Health, London.

Department of Health (1996a) *The Protection and Use of Patient Information: Guidance from the Department of Health*, Department of Health, London.

Department of Health (1996b) *Are You Entitled to Help with Health Costs?* Department of Health, Wetherby.

Department of Health (1996c) *Coordinating Community Mental Health Care: The Care Programme Approach*, Open University/Department of Health Social Services Inspectorate, Milton Keynes.

Dobson, R. (1996) 'Clients reject means tests', *Community Care*, 25–31 January, p. 9.

Downey, R. (1995) 'Survey reveals effect of community care on staff', *Community Care*, 30 March–5 April, p. 3.

Feldbaum, E. and Dick, R. (1997) *Electronic Patient Records, Smart Cards and Confidentiality*, Financial Times Pharmaceuticals and Healthcare Publishing, London.

Feil, N. (1992) *V/F Validation: the Feil Method: How to Help Disoriented Old-Old* (revised edn), Edward Feil Productions, Cleveland, Ohio.

General Medical Council (1993) *Professional Conduct and Discipline: Fitness to Practise*, General Medical Council, London.

Gilhooly, L. and McGhee, S. (1991) 'Medical records: practicalities and principles of patient possession', *Journal of Medical Ethics*, Vol. 17, pp. 138–43.

Glastonbury, B. (1985) *Computers in Social Work*, Macmillan, Basingstoke.

Glastonbury, B. (1995) 'Risk, information technology and social care', *Journal of the Centre for Human Service Technology*, Vol. 8, No. 3, pp. 2–10.

Gomm, R. (1989) *Counselling in the Renal Unit*, unpublished paper.

Hammond, P. (1997) 'Treating patients as equals has much to commend it, but how many of them know their oesophagus from their elbow?', *Independent: tabloid supplement*, 2 January, p. 3.

Harris, V. (1994) *Review of 'The Care and Treatment of Christopher Clunis': A Black Perspective*, Race Equality Unit, National Institute for Social Work, London.

Hogg, C. (1994) *Beyond the Patient's Charter: A Practical Guide for People Working in the Health Service*, Health Rights, London.

Home Office (1996a) *Consultative Paper on EU Data Protection Directive*, Home Office, London.

Home Office (1996b) *Protecting the Public*, HMSO, London.

Inskipp, F. (1988) *Counselling Skills*, National Extension College, Cambridge.

Kent, I. (1996) 'Reporting back', *Community Care*, 22–28 February, pp. 18–19.

Knight, B. (1993) *Voluntary Action* (Centris report), HMSO, London.

Kohner, N. (1996) *The Moral Maze of Practice: A Stimulus for Reflection and Discussion*, King's Fund, London.

Law Society/British Medical Association (1995) *Assessment of Mental Capacity: Guidance for Doctors and Lawyers*, British Medical Association, London.

Lifeline (1996) *Grandpa Smackhead Jones: The Oldest Junkie in the World*, Lifeline, Manchester.

McIver, S. and Martin, G. (1996) 'Unchartered territory', *Health Services Journal*, 19 September, pp. 24–5.

Muijen, M. (1995) 'Scare in the community: Part five: care of mentally ill people', *Community Care*, 7–13 September, supplement pp. i–viii.

National Health Service Executive (1991) *Access to Health Records Act 1990: A Guide for the NHS*, NHSE, London.

National Health Service Executive (1995) *Handling Confidential Information in Contracting: A Code of Practice*, NHSE, Leeds.

National Health Service Executive (1996a) *Complaints. Listening. Acting. Improving: Guidance on Implementation of the NHS Complaints Procedures*, Department of Health, Leeds.

National Health Service Executive (1996b) *Promoting Clinical Effectiveness*, Department of Health, Leeds.

National Health Service Training Directorate (1995) *Just for the Record: A Guide to Record Keeping for Health Care Professionals*, NHSTD, Bristol.

Northern Ireland Office (1991) *Care Management: Guide on Assessment and the Provision of Community Care*, Northern Ireland Office, Belfast.

Powell, T. (1992) *The Mental Health Handbook*, Winslow Press, Bicester.

Rapaport, J. (1996) 'Confidentiality and mental health care', *Practice Nursing*, Vol. 7, No. 6, pp. 12–14.

Ritchie, J., Dick, D. and Lingham, R. (1994) *The Report of the Inquiry into the Care and Treatment of Christopher Clunis*, HMSO, London.

Royal College of Psychiatrists (1996) *Report of the Confidential Inquiry into Homicides and Suicides by Mentally Ill People* (Boyd report), Royal College of Psychiatrists for the Confidential Inquiry into Homicides and Suicides by Mentally Ill People, London.

Scottish Home and Health Department (1989) *Confidentiality of Personal Health Information*, Scottish Home and Health Department, Edinburgh.

Shepherd, G., Murray, A. and Muijen, M. (1994) *Relative Values: Differing Views of Users, Family Carers and Professionals on Services for People with Schizophrenia in the Community*, Sainsbury Centre for Mental Health, London.

Silicon Bridge Research (1997) *The EPR Report*, Silicon Bridge Research, London.

Social Work Services Group (1989) *Code on Confidentiality of Social Work Records*, Social Work Services Group, Edinburgh.

Stone, A. (1984) *Law, Psychiatry and Morality*, American Psychiatry Press, New York.

Thompson, A. (1995) 'Tablets of stone', *Community Care*, 12–18 October, pp. 14–15.

United Kingdom Central Council for Nursing, Midwifery and Health Visiting (1993) *Confidentiality: An Elaboration of Clause 9 of the UKCC's Code of Professional Conduct*, UKCC, London.

Valios, N. (1996) 'Assessment queries "offensive" says client', *Community Care*, 2–8 May, p. 9.

Villeneau, L. (1994) 'Confidentiality', in *Mindfile 3: Practice Guidelines*, MIND, London.

Waller, T. (1993) *Drugswork 5: Working with GPs*, Institute for Study of Drug Dependence, London.

Walshe, K. and Ham, C. (1997) 'Who's acting on the evidence?', *Health Services Journal*, 3 April, pp. 22–5.

Watson, J. and Taylor, R. (1996) 'Standard practice', *Community Care*, 8–14 February, pp. 28–9.

Willis, J. (1997) 'Suspicious minds', *Health Services Journal*, 30 January, p. 8.

Acknowledgements

Grateful acknowledgement is made to the following sources for permission to reproduce material in this unit:

Text

pp. 94–5: Valios, N. (1996) 'Assessment queries "offensive" says client', *Community Care*, 2–8 May. Published by permission of the editor of *Community Care*.

Table

Table 3: Hogg, C. (1994) *Beyond the Patient's Charter: A Practical Guide for People Working in the Health Service*, Health Rights Ltd.

Illustrations

p. 65: Courtesy of Link 51 Storage Products Ltd; *p. 85 (left and middle)*: Courtesy of Hertfordshire County Council; *p. 85 (right)*: *NHS Citizens Charter: Complaints: Listening... Acting... Improving* (1996) NHS Executive, Department of Health; *p. 89*: Courtesy of Peter Cochrane; *p. 91*: Powell, T. (1992) *Mental Health Handbook*, Winslow Press, by permission of Trevor Powell; *pp. 100–01*: Courtesy of Lifeline Manchester.

Unit 20
Being Accountable

Prepared for the course team by Roger Gomm

While you are working on Unit 20, you will need:
- Course Reader
- Offprints Book
- Care in the UK
- Wallchart

Contents

Introduction

This unit is about accountability. To be accountable means that a person or an agency can be judged as to whether they have done what should have been done. Recorded information is an important source of evidence for accountability and in this respect this unit follows on directly from the last.

Signs like this on the back of lorries make drivers accountable for the quality of their driving. A similar function is performed by name badges for health and care staff and checkout staff in supermarkets, by the numbers worn by uniformed police officers, by the Cones Hotline advertised on the side of motorways, and even by the registration number of your car, if you have one. Everyone seems to be travelling down the road of accountability

'Accountability' seems to be the word on everyone's lips in health and social care contexts, and that is one reason why it is an important topic for this course. But why should this be?

1   Most health and social care services are funded from public sources and this means that an account is required of how the money is spent and how sensibly it is spent.

2   You have seen from other units of the course (Unit 18 for example) that just who is and who should be in the driving seat in health and social care contexts is a matter of some dispute: professionals or managers, central government or local people, workers or clients, purchasers or providers. Where control is contested so also will be accountability in the form of the question 'Who should practitioners or agencies be accountable to?'

3   Health and social care services often deal with people who are vulnerable and not in a position to look after their own interests. Overseeing their welfare is another aspect of accountability. You have already considered this with regard to the registration of residential and nursing homes and of childminders in Unit 8.

Section 1 of this unit looks at the ways in which people can be 'held to account' and the different directions in which accountability may lie. It goes on to consider one of those directions: accountability to the public, who claim a right to see that public money is being spent for purposes of which they approve. This is not quite the same matter as being accountable to the people who use services. That was dealt with in Unit 18.

Section 2 examines why it is that during the 1990s the accountability of practitioners and agencies in health and social care became such an important issue.

Section 3 considers what it is like to be made accountable. It does this first by returning to look at the job of Usha Ayer, whom you met in Unit 18. Who is she accountable to and how? Then it looks at a case study of a residential care worker dismissed from his job. This case study illustrates how difficult it sometimes is to decide whether an organisation or an individual is to blame for an adverse occurrence. Professional accountability is then considered through examining the experiences of nurses who feel that they are accountable for matters over which they have no control.

Section 4 looks at how people who work in health and social care respond to being accountable. Sometimes they do this through adopting tactics which are called 'defensive practice' and which subvert attempts to make them accountable. Sometimes they bring their employing organisation to account in an attempt to change the circumstances of their work so that they can better do what they are responsible for doing. Under some conditions workers in health and social care welcome accountability. The section examines the conditions under which practitioners find accountability acceptable, and how appropriate structures of accountability might promote good-quality care.

Core questions

- What does it mean to be accountable?

- Why has there been pressure to increase the level of accountability in health and social care?

- What problems arise for people and agencies who are made accountable and how do they respond to these?

- How might accountability be organised to promote high-quality care?

Section 1
The meanings of accountability

Being accountable means that you have an obligation to describe and justify your actions to others so that they can judge whether you have fulfilled your duties adequately. It usually also implies that if you are found wanting, something unpleasant will happen to you. But, equally, unless you are accountable, you can't receive recognition for what you do well. Accountability would be a trivial idea if all it meant was that people had to describe and explain their actions, and nothing ever happened as a result. So, in effect, accountability implies that someone's or some agency's activities are to some degree subject to limitation and control by others.

Perhaps the most familiar example of accountability, familiar from police dramas, is the way in which everyone is potentially accountable under the criminal law. People suspected of a crime are made to give an account of themselves through a police interview. If matters go further than this they will have to give an account of themselves in court. At the same time the police are accountable for showing that their suspicions were well founded and their conduct in arresting and interrogating the suspect was proper. Their actions can be challenged through the police complaints procedures and through other means. The Crown Prosecution Service (in England, Wales and Northern Ireland; the Procurator Fiscal in Scotland) is accountable for its decisions to prosecute. This is largely on the basis of whether the expense was justified by the verdict. Each court which tries the case is accountable to a superior court should the case follow a route of appeals. In addition, solicitors can be made accountable for the adequacy of their performance through the Law Society, and barristers accountable for theirs through the Bar Council. That may sound complicated, but it is actually a rather simple and tidy system by comparison with accountability in health and social care contexts, as you will see.

Key points

- Being accountable means having an obligation to describe and justify actions, so that others can judge whether duties have been fulfilled adequately.

- It usually implies that something important will happen because the judgement has been made.

1.1 Directions of accountability

'Accountable to whom?' is always an important issue. There are a large number of directions in which someone or some agency might be accountable, often at the same time.

Activity 1   *Webs of accountability*

Allow about 5 minutes   Think of a health or social care worker, agency or volunteer and write their name or job title in the middle of a sheet of paper. Then think of the various other people or bodies who might judge their performance and whose judgements might have some effect. Write these around the outside and draw lines between the name in the centre and all these other people or bodies. Figure 1 gives you an example, although it is much more complicated than the web you will produce.

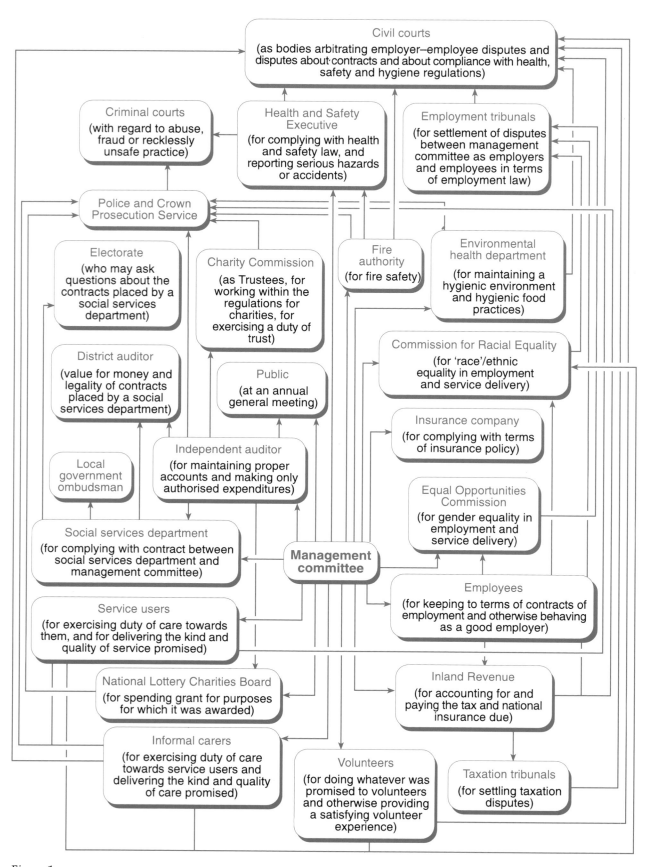

Figure 1
The web of accountability for the management committee of a day centre for people with dementia

Comment   The web of accountability will be different for different agencies and different practitioners. But your response will probably contain at least some of the kinds of directions of accountability which are listed next.

Here are some directions of accountability which often apply to health and social care practitioners and agencies. As you will see from the list it is sometimes difficult to distinguish one from another.

Public accountability. To some extent the mass media make agencies publicly accountable. You saw this in Unit 19 in relation to media coverage of public inquiries into murders by people with psychiatric diagnoses (Muijen, 1995). However, 'the public' is a large and diverse group, so effective public accountability usually requires some system for nominating people to represent the 'public interest' – through elections perhaps. Although the public hardly appear in the day centre example (Figure 1), management committee members are elected at a public annual general meeting, and there they have to give a 'public account' of their activities. Sometimes there are one or more regulatory agencies who act 'in the public interest' (see below). In Figure 1 you can see various 'public authorities' which have an interest in the day centre, and perhaps provide funds for it or refer clients to it or have duties in regulating its activities. They in turn are publicly accountable. For example, the social services department is accountable because it is run by a locally elected council. The legal system is a general-purpose regulator (see below). It administers laws which have been made by politicians who are publicly accountable in and through Parliament.

Legal accountability. This means accountability to the courts and to other judicial bodies such as employment tribunals, the tribunals which arbitrate disputes about welfare benefits or, in England, Wales and Northern Ireland, the tribunals to which people detained under mental health legislation can appeal against their detention (Department of Health, 1996). Whatever their origin, most disputes about whether some agency has fulfilled its obligations can end up in the courts. The criminal law makes everyone accountable and crimes committed in the course of health or social care work are still crimes.

Accountability to regulators and inspectors. For example, nursing and residential homes are accountable to the independent inspectorates of the health authority and the social services (or social work) authority respectively, although often these operate as a single, joint inspectorate. You considered this form of regulation in Unit 8. But the example in Figure 1 included other regulators and inspectors. There is also the fire safety authority, the environmental health department of a local authority, the Charity Commission, the Commission for Racial Equality and the Equal Opportunities Commission, should anyone care to make a complaint about gender or ethnic discrimination at the centre.

 Other important regulators and inspectorates in health and social care are listed in Section 3 'Regulation and Inspection' of Care in the UK. You might like to look at the relevant section now. In the lists of references for this course you will often come across reports from bodies such as these. All publicly funded bodies are subject to independent financial audit as well, and systems of public inquiry when things go wrong.

Accountability to central government. For example, central government issues guidance and sets performance targets for most public agencies. The latter have to provide information so that they can be judged in terms of whether they are following the guidance or meeting the targets. In this course you have often encountered the official guidance on implementing the NHS and Community Care Act 1990 (Department of Health Social Services Inspectorate/Scottish Office

Social Work Services Group, 1991; Northern Ireland Office, 1991). The government, of course, represents itself here as acting in the 'public interest'. Regulators (see above) often inspect to see whether performance targets imposed by central government are being met, and often advise central government as to what they should be.

Accountability as a contractor. Contracts between purchasers and providers (see Units 3, 10 and 18) make providers accountable for doing whatever they promise the purchasers in the contract, and vice versa. The day centre in Figure 1 has a grant from the National Lottery Charities Board with conditions to match.

Accountability as an employee or employer. A contract of employment makes an employee of a health or care agency accountable for doing whatever their contract specifies, and this is usually spelt out in greater detail in job descriptions and operational policies. Often what employees have to do is determined by the law, by central government guidance, by purchaser/provider contracts or by central government performance targets. Contracts of employment also make employers accountable to employees, and to various bodies such as the Health and Safety Executive, the various equal opportunities commissions (race, gender, disability and, in Northern Ireland, the Fair Employment Agency – see Care in the UK, Section 3), the Inland Revenue, and in the case of dispute, to the system of employment tribunals and to the civil courts. Such contracts exist in law, whether or not there is a piece of paper called a 'contract of employment'.

Accountability as a professional. Some health and social care workers are subject to regulatory bodies which maintain registers from which practitioners can be removed: for example, doctors (General Medical Council, 1993), nurses (United Kingdom Central Council for Nursing, Midwifery and Health Visiting, 1996a and b) and the professions allied to medicine, such as chiropodists, physiotherapists or occupational therapists (Council for the Professions Supplementary to Medicine, 1997). Professionals who are registered in this way are bound to follow their profession's codes of conduct and may be 'struck off' if they don't. Complaints can also be made about professionals to their professional body.

Market accountability. This is the idea that under market conditions the successful providers thrive and the unsuccessful go to the wall. It was a notion close to the heart of Conservative ministers from 1979 to 1997, and a major reason for creating the purchaser/provider splits (Unit 3 and Unit 18). It was not so well thought of by the incoming Labour government of 1997. It now seems to be widely agreed that the 'market' for health and care services in Britain doesn't really operate like commercial markets (Boyal and Darkins, 1994). However, the fact is that for care providers like Independent Nursing Services in Unit 3, unless they satisfy the purchasing authorities, the authorities will look elsewhere.

Accountability to service users through complaints procedures. Complaints procedures allow aggrieved service users to bring individual practitioners or agencies to account. When local complaints procedures fail, recourse may be had to the commissioners or ombudsmen for local government (local 'administration'), for the health service, or for Parliament. The work of the commissioner (ombudsman) for local administration is illustrated opposite, and Section 3 of Care in the UK gives further details. In addition, or alternatively, when complaints procedures fail, recourse may be had to the courts. In the case of professional workers, complaints may also be made to their professional body.

Ombudsman attacks Lambeth in child case

Senior social services managers in a London borough have been slated by the ombudsman after a child protection case was dropped without investigation or a decision to shelve the case.

The ombudsman has ordered Lambeth to pay £2,000 to parents who had to live for over a year with 'the grinding anxiety' surrounding unspecified allegations about their daughter.

The embattled borough's social services department was called in by teachers after they noticed a bump under the five year old's eye. She was also often tired and lethargic, complained of stomach aches and masturbated in class.

The ombudsman found that child protection staff acted promptly to arrange a familiarisation meeting but the sudden cancellation of a diagnostic meeting due to staff illness led to the case effectively being dropped without the parents being told. There was no assessment of whether the family needed counselling or support.

Letters from the mother to the director, David Pope, were passed to other senior officers but produced no meaningful response for up to six months.

The ombudsman said the case exposed 'serious lapses in procedure and gross failure by senior managers to follow up initial enquiries (and) to check that the child protection procedures had been followed adequately'.

(*Care Weekly*, 1995, p. 3)

The main interest of the various ombudsmen is maladministration. They investigate complaints that authorities have not followed the rules they should have followed, whether these rules are laid down by law, by central government guidance or by the authority itself. This case concerns the ombudsman or commissioner for local government administration in England. There are other ombudsmen for health and for central government activity (see Care in the UK, Section 3).

Accountability to service users. This may be through involving service user organisations or representatives in the planning, management, monitoring and evaluation of services (see Unit 18). In addition, accountability to service users may derive from what is promised to them in a care plan, or what promises practitioners make verbally. The care plan for Arthur Durrant which you read in Unit 19 made certain promises on behalf of social services. Because they were written down, failure to honour them would be relatively easy to complain about. It is much more difficult to hold practitioners to verbal undertakings which are unrecorded.

As you can see, people who work in health and social care may be accountable in numerous different ways, sometimes as individuals, and sometimes because the agency they work for is made accountable. There are very few situations in which only one kind of accountability applies. Indeed, it was very difficult to write a logical list, since these modes of accountability run into each other.

1.2 Accountability structures

Accountability in any serious sense suggests what can be called 'accountability structures' (The Open University, 1996, p. 64). As the example from the criminal justice system earlier suggested, fully developed accountability structures often involve checks and balances whereby those who hold others to account are in their turn held to account by yet others.

Any accountability structure will have some of the features shown in the box below.

The main features of accountability structures

1   There will be *explicit statements about responsibilities*. These might be written into job descriptions, contracts and/or codes of practice, or operational policies, or encoded into law. Required performance might be specified in terms of performance targets or statements of the outcomes someone is supposed to achieve.

2   There will be *procedures for making performance or outcomes observable*. These might include surveillance, supervision or periodic inspection and are most likely to include the requirement for people to make records of their activities. You considered monitoring data in Unit 18, Activity 15, and records in general in Unit 19.

3   There are likely to be *penalties and sanctions* against inadequate performance and there may also be *rewards* for excellent performance.

4   There will be *mechanisms for bringing someone or some organisation to account*. Examples include appraisal and supervision, annual reports on performance, audits and complaints procedures, and the procedures listed below.

5   To protect people against unjust accusations, there are likely to be *formal procedures for investigating alleged shortcomings*. Examples include disciplinary hearings, grievance procedures, committees of inquiry, the procedures of the civil and criminal law, and various systems of appeal from one decision-making body to another.

To make this abstract list more concrete, consider the financial accountability of a voluntary sector organisation given in the box below.

Financial accountability for a voluntary sector organisation

1   There will be *explicit statements about responsibilities* in its constitution, in the terms of its grants and contracts, in agreements made and minuted in its meetings:
    – to spend money on this and not on that
    – to record income and expenditure in particular ways and to render these accounts up for audit
    – to make the accounts public – and if the organisation is a charity (England, Wales and Northern Ireland) to send copies to the Charity Commission (Charity Commissioners for England and Wales, 1996); if it is a company to send accounts to the Registrar of Companies; and if it is a friendly society or co-operative to the Registrar for Friendly Societies (Phillips, 1994).

2   There will be *procedures for making performance or outcomes observable*:
    – the written accounts themselves and all the documentary evidence which goes with them, such as invoices and petty cash books
    – the audit by an independent auditor
    – the rendering of accounts to funding bodies
    – the public presentation of accounts.

3   There will be *penalties and sanctions* against inadequate performance. Overspends and underspends are likely to have consequences for the future funding of the agency, and expenditure on things not authorised may be fraud. For example, in 1996 Newcastle MIND lost its contract to provide mental health care because it had been spending money from the statutory agencies on services it was not contracted to provide, and failed to keep adequate accounts (Whiteley, 1996).

4   There will be *mechanisms for bringing to account*. The audit is the most important of these.

5   There will be *formal procedures for investigating alleged shortcomings*. These are as listed under 2 and, in the case of disputes, there will be awkward meetings with funders, inquiries by the Charity Commission, or court appearances if fraud is an issue. There will also be agency disciplinary procedures for investigating the conduct of staff, employment tribunals that deal with unfair dismissal, appeals from one court to another, and so on.

Activity 2   Your experience of accountability

Allow about 15 minutes   The purpose of this activity is for you to relate what you going to read in this unit to your own experiences. Select a situation where you are, or have been, the person who is accountable. For preference choose a health or welfare context, but if this is not possible, an example from education, or housing, or as a provider or consumer of goods and services, or as an employee in an office or factory will do. You don't have to place yourself among the employees; patients are accountable to health services, students to educational institutions, benefits claimants to the Benefits Agency, and so on.

When you have chosen your example, work through the items in the box outlining the features of accountability structures and note down anything in your example which corresponds with what is listed there. Where there are no correspondences ask yourself whether the absence of this element of accountability is a good or bad thing.

There will be no comment for this activity, but keep your notes because you will be asked to use them again in a later one.

1.3 Trust and accountability

Something you might have thought of in doing the last activity is that elaborate structures of accountability suggest that people cannot be trusted to do what they are supposed to do without such devices. It is worth considering this in a little more detail.

Activity 3   **From mutual trust to formal accountability**

Allow about 15 minutes

For this activity find Offprint 28, 'Empowering empowerment: professionals and self-advocacy projects', by Jan Wallcraft. The story she tells is of a project which was transformed into something very different from what the originators wanted. The same thing happened to one of the groups that formed the basis for the fictional Phoenix Centre in Unit 18. However, the story here is about how Wallcraft's project was transformed from one in which everything could be done by informal mutual agreement among people who trusted each other, into one in which accountability was put on a formal basis. Read the article and jot down your ideas about:

(a)   whether this transformation was inevitable or avoidable

(b)   whether it was justifiable.

Comment   (a)   This transformation was almost inevitable once the group received funding from a public source. Public funding nearly always brings a measure of accountability for how the money is spent, if only because the statutory authorities or the charitable organisations which fund public services are accountable for how they themselves have spent public money.

It was also inevitable once the group became responsible for the welfare of more than its founder members: responsible as employers and as providers of a service to others. In providing finance to such organisations, social services authorities and health authorities are extending their own 'duty of care', for which they are accountable. Hence their desire to make contractors accountable for safety, confidentiality, fairness of treatment, and so on. Sometimes statutory authorities also require contractors to make themselves accountable to those who use their services (see Unit 18).

(b)   There is a good case for saying that it would have been unjustifiable to have funded this group from public sources and to have allowed it to go on operating in the original unaccountable way, even though this blighted the dream of the original group.

The original self-advocacy group was a collection of people who were in agreement with each other. As a group they had some responsibilities for each other, but none for anyone else. This was the kind of organisation in which people could reach agreements informally and trust each other to carry out what they had promised to do. Failing that, if there were disagreements and broken promises these could be settled by aggrieved people leaving the group. Indeed, if the group had collapsed in dissension, then only those who were members would have been affected. So long as they agreed with each other there was no great need for rules or constitutions, written job descriptions or much else to put the accountability of members on a more formal footing. Nonetheless, it is wise for even the most informal groups to have some ground rules in terms of which disagreements can be resolved (The Open University, 1992).

However, this situation changed when the group received funding from a public source in order to supply a public service. Then they were required to do proper budgeting, keep proper accounts and submit them to audit; to draw up and keep to the kinds of rules about employees that employers are supposed to abide by, and make themselves accountable to the Inland Revenue for the payment of PAYE taxation. Although this is not mentioned in the article, presumably the group would have been required to write and commit themselves to policy documents about, for example, equal opportunities, confidentiality and user involvement; to devise complaints procedures and provide monitoring information so that the funding organisation could judge whether the project was achieving the objectives it was funded for. Assuming that the group was in England, Wales or Northern Ireland and sought and gained charitable status, then its management committee would have become accountable as 'trustees' to the Charity Commission; accountable for spending money only to achieve ends defined as 'charitable' and for following the rules of a constitution agreed by the Commission.

The article does mention that the group had to draw up and follow a written constitution and among other things this would define the proper procedures for making decisions. Through the minutes of its meetings, then, the group became accountable for showing that decisions were made correctly according to the constitution, consistent with the charitable status of the organisation and according to their agreement with the funding body – and not on the whim or fancy of someone who just felt like making any old decision. The same constitution would probably make the new agency accountable to 'the public' by having a public annual general meeting at which its accounts would be displayed and a report of its work given. You saw much of this in Unit 18 when the development of the Phoenix Centre was discussed.

It is important to recognise that when a statutory authority, such as a health authority, social services or social work department or a Northern Ireland board, contracts out a service, it does not cease to have a duty of care towards the people who use the service. This has always been the case. When, for example, abuse occurs in an independent children's home, or within fostering arrangements, blame still attaches to the social services department which placed the child in these circumstances. You can see this from the article reproduced overleaf. It shows the accountability of social services departments for ensuring that foster parents are people who can be trusted with the welfare of children. As you read it, look out for the various ways in which social services departments have been made accountable for their errors in this case, and how their responsibilities are to be tightened up – the first characteristic of an accountability structure shown in the box in Section 1.2.

Abuse checks on all foster parents

Colin Brown and Roger Dobson

Checks on thousands of foster parents could be made in a national crackdown on paedophiles ordered by the Government last night after the conviction of a man who was allowed to foster children, even though social workers knew he had a conviction for indecent assault on a 12-year-old boy.

Roger Saint yesterday was sentenced to six-and-a-half years imprisonment on 10 charges of indecent assault at Chester Crown Court. The scandal of child abuse disclosed in the case prompted the Government to promise to close loopholes in two child care acts which allowed Saint to care for the children he molested in spite of having a criminal record for child abuse. A ban on child abusers being allowed to foster or adopt children was announced by Paul Boateng, the health minister responsible for child care. Sir Herbert Laming, the Chief Inspector of Social Services, was also asked to consider an urgent review.

Local authorities are responsible for the care of 49,000 children, including 32,000 who were placed with foster parents. A Whitehall source said: 'It is not retrospective, but we are aware that people could have convictions for child abuse and we are going to tackle it.'

The action will be 'spelled out' in guidelines to the authorities, but it is expected they will be asked to carry out checks to make sure there are no further cases of known paedophiles fostering children.

The court heard that Saint was allowed to foster four children from Tower Hamlets, east London, in 1988; in 1991 he fostered another four from North Yorkshire; and he later fostered one child from Greenwich, south London, and another from North Tyneside. Social workers in each authority were aware of his criminal record from 25 years earlier. They decided he was no longer a risk to the children. Saint, 50, was jailed for what the judge says was the 'persistent and determined' sexual abuse of boys in his care over 13 years.

Michael Farmer QC, prosecuting, said local authorities had continued sending children into the care of Saint and his wife Carol despite knowing of the conviction. The now-defunct Clwyd County Council allowed him to continue as a member of their fostering and adoption panel despite being told of the offence

[...]

A 10-month investigation followed up 400 lines of inquiry. The court was told Saint's case was to be looked at by the North Wales child abuse tribunal, which is examining allegations of abuse of up to 200 children at homes in the area.

'This is a truly horrific case. This new government will not tolerate a loophole in the law that allows local authorities to place children for foster care or adoption with convicted child abusers, which happened in this case,' said Mr Boateng.

The loophole under the 1989 Children Act and the 1976 Adoption Act requires local authorities to check whether people who foster or adopt have criminal records, but gives them discretion to place children with convicted child abusers. That discretion will be removed. 'It beggars belief that any social worker would do that, but some obviously did. We must stop that ever happening again,' Mr Boateng said.

(*Independent*, 24 May 1997, p. 1)

Key points

- When public money is dispensed it is usually accompanied by an obligation to account for how it is spent.

- When the statutory purchasers of health or social care services issue contracts to providers, they remain accountable for the welfare of the people who use the services.

- Hence contracts usually come with conditions which make the provider accountable to purchasers for showing that their duty of care has been fulfilled.

1.4 Public accountability, performance indicators and charters

Most people would agree with the general principle that if services are funded with public money, they should be made publicly accountable for their performance. An increasingly common way of attempting to do this, across public services as a whole, is for central government to set up criteria for performance and to require public services to provide information on whether, or how far, they are meeting them.

You can hardly fail to be aware of what are the most newsworthy performance indicators of all: the so-called 'league tables' of educational performance which are published about the achievements of individual schools and educational authorities. There are over 200 central government performance indicators for NHS trusts and health authorities (Merry, 1996, p. 51). Some of these derive from the English Health of the Nation programme (Department of Health, 1992) and the equivalents for the other nations of the UK (Health Promotion Wales, 1990; Scottish Office, 1992; Department of Health and Social Services Northern Ireland, 1992), others from the Patient's Charter, and yet others are about the use of resources including the much disliked 'efficiency index' for NHS trusts.

1991

In reading Offprint 24, the community care plan for mental health (Unit 18), you will have noticed a reference to an Audit Commission report on case loads for community mental health workers. The Audit Commission for England and Wales and the Accounts Commission for Scotland provide information in terms of which the performance of different health (and social services or social work) agencies can be made accountable by comparison with each other – so-called 'benchmarking'. The National Health Service Advisory Service, which includes the Drug Advisory Service, plays a rather similar role (Merry, 1996, p. 191). In Scotland there are performance indicators for general practice as well as for hospitals (National Health Service Management Executive (Scotland), 1997). And across the UK there are performance criteria for recruiting workers and serving patients from minority ethnic groups in a programme driven by the Ethnic Health Unit at the Department of Health (National Health Service Executive, 1994). The Local Government Management Board (1995) co-ordinates a similar initiative for local authorities in England and Wales.

Similarly, there are performance indicators and targets for local authorities including social and social work services, housing, environmental health, probation and the police (Audit Commission, 1995). The first set of performance indicators for social services (England for 1994) were relatively simple. There were:

- the percentage of older people helped to live at home
- the percentage of older people supported in residential accommodation
- the percentage of adults known by the local authority to have physical disabilities
- the percentage of adults with physical disabilities helped to live at home
- the nights of respite care per 1000 adults.

Others will be added. The Eastern Health and Social Services Board in Northern Ireland has piloted a much more comprehensive set of standards and indicators for social care services (Eastern Health and Social Services Board, 1995) which is serving as a model for practice elsewhere. Inspections by the Social Services Inspectorate (England and Wales), by the separate Inspectorate for Northern Ireland, and by the Scottish Social Work Inspectorate provide benchmarking information in addition to that produced by the Audit and the Accounts Commission reports.

Performance indicators are often criticised for creating 'perverse incentives'. For example, the NHS efficiency index is criticised for encouraging NHS trusts to prioritise quantity and cost over quality (National Association of Health Authorities and Trusts, 1997), although less so now than in its original, 1992, form. And performance indicators are seen to lead to simplistic judgements about the performance of different agencies without fully taking their particular circumstances into consideration (Combes, 1995). Nonetheless, it does seem important that decision makers and the public should know, for example, that, 'Some councils were seen to provide ten times more respite than others' and that, '... Liverpool council provides almost four times more respite care than neighbouring Knowsley' (Combes, 1995, p.1).

1991

For the health service one of the most important sources of performance targets has been the Patient's Charter (Department of Health, 1991b, 1995a, 1995b), to which you were introduced in Unit 10 (see the next box). The next activity asks you to consider the role of the Patient's Charter in making health services accountable to patients and the public. For the activity you will need Offprint 29 'Unchartered territory' by Shirley McIver and Geraldine Martin. It is about the Patient's Charter, which lists what patients have a right to expect from the NHS. The offprint is concerned with the 1995 version of the charter. In 1999 there will be a new version which will include some obligations for patients for the first time. But in terms of making health services accountable to the public, both old and new have the function of making 'explicit statements about responsibilities'. As you saw from the box on accountabilities (Section 1.2), this is an essential first step in making services accountable. McIver and Martin are concerned that the monitoring of whether these responsibilities have been discharged is not

William Waldegrave, Minister for Health, launching the Patient's Charter

as effective as it might be. In terms of the box on accountability, their concerns are about the 'procedures for making performance or outcomes observable'. If these are deficient, then the third feature of an accountability structure cannot work. If you don't know how well a service is operating, then you have no basis for praising it, complaining about it, imposing sanctions, and so on.

Performance indicators from the Patient's Charter

The Patient's Charter has generated a number of performance indicators for NHS trusts which allow them to be ranked in league tables, not by the government but by the newspapers.

For example:

- percentage of outpatients admitted within 13 weeks of referral (O/P)

- percentage of outpatients not turning up for their appointment (N/S)

- percentage of patients needing to be inpatients admitted within three months of this need being decided (ADM).

In the newspaper league table for 1995–6 (*Guardian*, 11 July 1997), Stockport Acute Services came top and Forest Health Care (Waltham Forest) came bottom when all three ratings were combined, although some NHS trusts did better than Stockport or worse than Forest on particular indicators.

	O/P	N/S	ADM
Stockport Acute Services	81%	10%	70%
Forest Health Care	68%	18%	70%

These indicators are not a straightforward measure of the efficiency of different trusts. They also reflect the fact that different trusts experience higher or lower demands for treatment, are more or less well resourced, and have some discretion, for example, over what they count as 13 weeks from the date of referral.

The indicator for patients not turning up for appointments led the Labour government of 1997 to propose adding obligations for patients to the next version of the Patient's Charter which will appear in 1999. Non-attendance costs the NHS something like £500 million a year.

Activity 4   **Accountability through the Patient's Charter**

Allow about 25 minutes   Read Offprint 29 'Unchartered territory'.

(a)   Did you already know what your rights as a patient were under the Patient's Charter?

(b)   How might knowing your rights affect you as a patient?

(c)   Jot down some notes on the authors' concerns about the accountability of health services for delivering the Patient's Charter and what they suggest as a remedy.

Comment (a) In 1994 it appears that 40 per cent of the adult population had never heard of the Patient's Charter and of those who had heard of it, only a few could say what it contained (National Opinion Polls, 1994). You probably couldn't have recited all eight charter points accurately before reading the article.

(b) The charter does strengthen your position *as a patient* insofar as you can complain: 'the charter promised me this, but you have not delivered it'. And if those who provide services know this kind of complaint is likely to be made, they are likely to behave in ways that prevent the need for such complaints (Institute for Health Services Management, 1993). The same charter statements also imply standards for dealing with complaints (Department of Health, 1995c; National Health Service Executive, 1996a, 1996b).

(c) However, the offprint was actually pitched in terms of accountability to people in their roles *as citizens* with a right to be informed about how well services financed with their money are being run. The interests of people actually using services are not necessarily the same as those of 'the public' whose tax is paying for the services. The authors' main concern was the fact that health services themselves provide the information against which they are to be judged. They obviously do not trust health authorities or NHS trusts to report accurately and honestly on their own performance: 'how can the public trust data which is not independently validated?' The remedy they suggest is one commonly used when there is some doubt as to whether agencies can be trusted to be 'self-regulating': invent an independent regulatory body. People are now quite used to Ofwat, Ofgas, Ofsted, Ofthis and Ofthat, and in Unit 8 you encountered the local independent inspection units for nursing and residential homes.

In 1996 the outgoing Conservative government was considering either privatising inspection, or transferring it to trading standards departments, on the grounds that local social services inspection teams were not independent enough (Eaton, 1996). What McIver and Martin suggest is more of the same. Given their personal connections with the Association of Community Health Councils for England and Wales (1995), they may be arguing for an enhanced role for these, as well as making an explicit suggestion to expand the role of the 'statutory commissioners' (ombudsmen).

The comment referred to yet another way in which health services are made accountable. This is through the activities of local Community Health Councils in England and Wales, and Local Health Councils in Scotland (there are no equivalent bodies in Northern Ireland). Half the membership is nominated by the local authorities (which are themselves democratically elected), one-third by ballot in the voluntary sector, and the remainder appointed by the NHS Executive on the basis of local recommendations. They are independent of their health authority (or board) and of the NHS trusts they monitor. In monitoring NHS trusts they use centrally imposed performance criteria as well as criteria of their own, and they are involved in the procedures for locality commissioning (see Unit 18), and assist aggrieved patients to make complaints about health services (McKechnie, 1996a, 1996b).

 Equivalent to the Patient's Charter for health services are the community care charters for social services and social work departments. However, these have been drawn up locally within a framework imposed by central government (Department of Health Social Services Inspectorate, 1994) rather than being imposed *en bloc* from above, so they differ from area to area. When you read Offprint 26, which is a synopsis of a community care plan for mental health, you may have noticed that the social services department intended in future to monitor its own performance in terms of its charter commitments. You might like to look at this again. Up to a point this social services authority is making itself publicly accountable, and accountable to organised groups of service users and to other agencies in the health and care field, through the very process of community care planning. One year it commits itself to achieving certain outcomes. The next it gives an account of how far it has achieved them. The extract below illustrates how another local authority makes itself accountable to its council tax payers by showing how it has met Audit Commission performance targets. Of course, many provider agencies have their own 'service user charters' as well, with varying degrees of commitment to monitor their own performance, and varying systems of being monitored externally.

MacIver and Martin also suggest that 'ordinary people' should be more involved both in setting the standards and monitoring performance. You may remember the 'lay' inspectors in the system for regulating residential and nursing homes (Unit 8). This, however, raises a series of questions:

Expertise. Do ordinary people have the expertise to set standards for and monitor the performance of services where this involves esoteric knowledge and complex clinical, administrative and financial decision making?

Motivation. How far are ordinary people willing to invest a great deal of time and effort in such activities? Wouldn't most people prefer someone else to do it on their behalf?

Figuring out Cambridge City Council - How we performed in 1995-96

We are publishing information about how we performed in 1995-96. The questions are set by Audit Commission, and for most of them, you can compare our performance with the previous year.

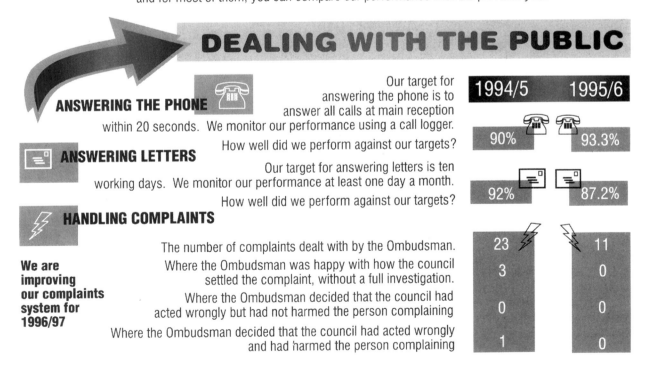

How Cambridge City Council makes itself accountable to its council tax payers in terms of Audit Commission performance indicators. This comes from a booklet sent to all households (Cambridge City Council, 1996, p. 2)

Representativeness. If lay people with sufficient expertise and motivation can be found to monitor service performance, just how representative would they be of people in general? How could they gain any mandate from the public to act on its behalf, and through what mechanisms could they report back their findings to 'the public'?

The use of 'citizens' juries' to inform the planning of health and social care suggests that 'ordinary people' can quite quickly develop the expertise necessary if they are provided with the relevant information in a form they can understand. Citizens' juries developed first in Germany and the USA and are increasingly being used in Britain to tap public opinion with regard to setting priorities for health care purchasing. This is sometimes used as an alternative or adjunct to the kinds of community care planning and locality commissioning procedures you read about in Unit 18. The following extract gives you a glimpse of what citizen jurors learn from the process, and what helps them to come to informed decisions. Read it now.

Open court

A citizens' jury on drug use proved an education for its participants and changed their view of how to tackle the problem. Joy Ogden reports.

Last week David Goldring's instincts were to 'go ballistic' with drug users. Police should take a tough line, clinics were too soft an option, drugs were a real danger. But that was last week.

This week he is not so sure. Four days on a citizens' jury set him thinking and now he believes – with almost evangelical fervour – that other people should be educated about drugs as he has been so that they too can come to an informed opinion. Most of his fellow jurors feel the same.

The way the jury heard the expert evidence and – in the light of what its members were told – changed their views carries important lessons for health authorities faced with difficult consultation processes on highly charged and complex issues.

Mr Goldring is a 33-year-old Afro-Caribbean finance officer, and was one of 16 jurors chosen at random to mirror the population of the south London borough of Lewisham.

[...]

Over four days at the end of April the jury heard testimonies from addicts, former addicts and recreational drug users. They weighed the evidence and cross-examined an impressive procession of expert witnesses from the health, education and police services ...

Lewisham council's policy officers, Brigitte Gohdes and Stella Clarke, took notes, then provided printed witness statements and summaries of issues raised at each day's debates, so jurors did not become overwhelmed by the volume of data. And there was a lot of information – sometimes conflicting – to process.

(Ogden, 1996, p. 12)

 The extract you have just read relates to a scheme run by the Local Government Management Board covering seven local authorities and their associated health authorities, called 'The Democracy Project', experimenting with different forms of local consultation. At the same time the King's Fund Institute was running three pilot projects in three different health authorities (*King's Fund News*, Summer 1997, pp. 1–6). There are other examples elsewhere (Brindle, 1995) as responses to the Conservative government's 'Local Voices' initiative (National Health Service Management Executive, 1992; Heginbotham, 1992). That was the instruction to health authorities to draw up their purchasing plans through a process of consultation involving the public (Unit 18).

Three problems were mentioned earlier with regard to effective public involvement. Properly managed, the process of citizen jury deliberations seems to deal with the issue of *expertise* (see also Brochie and Wann, 1993). In the end, David and his fellow jurors decided that spending money on prescribing methadone for drug addicts was a worthwhile use of health service money. As for *motivation*, just how many people would be prepared to spend four days sitting on a citizens' jury is an open question. The £50 payment made in Lewisham probably helped, but there has been a long-term decline in public participation in public affairs. Citizens' juries are not *representative* in the democratic sense of the term, which implies being elected by a constituency to represent them. But if, like court juries, they are selected at random, then they are more likely to be representative in the statistical sense of the term; that is, representing the range of different types of people in an area. They would certainly be more representative of the general public than the people who choose themselves to be involved in community care and locality commissioning planning, as described in Unit 18.

The issue of public accountability is a difficult one and is really about how public affairs should be organised in general, and how public decisions should be made and their effects evaluated when there are many different groups with many different and conflicting interests (Cooper *et al.*, 1995). *Public accountability* is a different matter from accountability to people who use services. To put the issue in the starkest possible way, in a typical area about 1 per cent of the population will be regarded as having learning difficulties, while around 40 per cent will be paying the taxes from which services for these people will be provided. The two groups are not mutually exclusive, of course. But this raises the question of which group services should be most accountable to. That's not an easy issue to decide.

Key points

- Publicly funded services imply public accountability – which is not the same as accountability to the people who use the services.

- Public accountability for health and social care services is an untidy matter, involving elements of electoral democracy (through elected local authorities), mechanisms of public involvement (through community care planning and locality commissioning), the publication of data in terms of performance indicators, and monitoring, inspection and regulation through bodies supposedly representing the public interest.

Study skills: Being accountable in your assignments

There is a kind of accountability involved in writing your TMAs, an implicit contract between you and the tutor. It goes like this: provided that you answer the question set, the tutor will read your answer carefully and award you marks for your knowledge and the quality of your writing. But if you don't answer the question set, the tutor writes 'irrelevant' in the margins and you get poor marks, even if you have said knowledgeable things. In effect, the TMA question represents the 'explicit statement of responsibilities', the first characteristic of an accountability structure which you read about earlier in this unit. Both you and the tutor are accountable to the way the TMA is worded. This comes out all the more clearly if you decide to appeal against your mark and a third party has to adjudicate on whether your answer does or doesn't meet the requirements of the question.

In other words, it is very important to pay attention to the details of the wording of assignment (and exam) questions. (This is the first of the seven stages of essay writing outlined in Section 2 of Chapter 6 of *The Good Study Guide*.) Even quite small differences in wording can make big differences to what you should write. Look, for example, at the two questions below.

1   What kinds of information do *potential* service users need in order to *access* services? Illustrate your answer with examples drawn from a particular health or social care service.

2   What kinds of information do service users need in order to *use* services *effectively*? Illustrate your answer with examples drawn from a particular health or social care service.

How many differences did you spot in the two questions? And more importantly, how does the emphasis of the second question differ from the first?

The only differences are the words 'potential' in question 1, and 'effectively' in question 2, and the replacement of 'access' by 'use'. Otherwise the two questions are identical. But the first is about information which makes services accessible to people who are not yet using them. The second is about information for people who are already using services (although you might argue that it includes potential users as well, since you can't use a service effectively if you don't know about it).

So would answers to the two questions be very different? First, stop and think of the health or social care service you would choose for the purposes of illustrating your answer. (That will make it easier to think about the kinds of information that might be needed.) Then look below at the list of kinds of information you might possibly think of discussing in an answer. Which of these kinds do you think should definitely be included in an answer? Which might be included if you have space and time? Which do you think can safely be left out?

First, consider question 1. Work down the column headed Q1 writing 1, 2 or 3 in the boxes.

1 = definitely include

2 = could include if there is space

3 = can safely leave out

Then do the same for question 2.

Kinds of information	Q1	Q2
• What service is available, where and when	1	2
• Who is eligible to use the service	1	1
• How to access the service	1	1
• What it is like to use the service	2	3
• What conditions the user must abide by	2	2

- Whether the service is free or charged for, and on what basis
- Whether the service requires disclosure of confidential information
- How the rules of confidentiality operate
- Options the service offers to its users
- What risks might arise from the service (e.g. surgical risks or drug side effects)
- Who to contact if there is a crisis or a query, and how and when
- How to make complaints about the service

The pattern of numbers in the boxes will depend partly on what service you had in mind. But in general the Q1 column is likely to have more 1s towards the top and more 3s towards the bottom, whereas the Q2 column is likely to be the other way around. What should come out clearly is that the kinds of information you would discuss in answering the two questions would be distinctly different. Yet the wording is almost identical. To make your essay 'accountable' to the title you always need to pay close attention to the wording.

Section 2

Increasing accountability in health and social care

There is no doubt that from the end of the 1980s onwards those who work in health and social care have been subjected to increased accountability. There are two main features of this and they are linked. They are consumerism and managerialism.

2.1 Consumerism

This period has seen the development of very assertive consumer movements among those who use health and social care services. You read about one aspect of this – the self-advocacy movement – in Unit 18. This is only part of a wider trend which includes much more vigorous campaigning by the pressure groups representing the interests of service users: for example Mencap, Age Concern, ENABLE or the Alzheimers Disease Society (McKechnie, 1996b). Their memberships go much further than the service users themselves, including carers, practitioners, academics, interested members of the public, and celebrities such as the late Princess Diana. Each group tries to make the headlines at least once a year when it publishes its annual report, and often more frequently, and the larger groups are well represented in Parliament by sympathetic MPs or members of the House of Lords.

Action by individual service users, whether supported by such groups or not, must also be added to the story. So, for example, in the NHS the number of complaints doubled between 1991 and 1995, and by 1994 it was paying out around £125 million per year in court and out-of-court settlements for costs and damages following lawsuits from patients and their relatives. Again, this is about double the bill for 1991 (Harris, 1996, p. 4). This figure is likely to increase dramatically as lawyers in England and Wales more frequently adopt the American 'no win, no fee' system whereby service users pay no legal costs if they are awarded no compensation (Berliner, 1997). There is little evidence that the quality of care in the NHS was twice as bad in 1995 as in 1991, and the general opinion is that this increase in complaints and lawsuits reflects a greater willingness by consumers to bring health services to account. Social services have also seen an increase in complaints and litigation (Department of Health Social Services Inspectorate, 1994), and particularly in the use of judicial review by the courts, which was something hardly ever used before the mid-1980s. The following box tells you something about judicial reviews and gives an example.

Judicial reviews

Judicial reviews are High Court hearings to establish whether an authority such as a health authority, board or trust, a government department or, as in the example below, a social services or social work authority has acted according to the law, and/or according to procedures it has committed itself to. They are used particularly to clarify what the law is when there is some doubt about this. Thus the findings of judicial reviews make law for the future (Public Law Project, 1994; Gordon, 1993, pp. 55–65).

For example, the way the Carers (Recognition and Services) Act 1995 was drafted left it unclear whether children who were informal carers were included and were entitled to an assessment of their needs as carers, or whether their entitlement to assessment under the Children Act 1989 excluded them from this. Newham Council interpreted the Carers Act to exclude young carers, and that left a 14-year-old, partially deaf girl having to wash her profoundly disabled sister in a washing-up bowl because the council refused to install a shower to assist with 'caring'. The judicial review was initiated by the child's mother and the 14-year-old, supported by the Carers National Association. The review found against Newham Council, which was ordered to install the shower and provide 17 days' respite care per year for the family. But the important outcome was that the case established that the needs of 'young carers' did fall under the Carers Act. In fact, Newham could, and probably should, have provided exactly the same under Section 17 of the Children Act: the shower to meet the needs of the younger sister, and respite care to meet the needs of the 14-year-old. These were their needs as children in both cases (Brindle, 1997).

The term 'consumer' was used advisedly above, because suing for redress is exactly what *consumers* do. It was part of Conservative government (1979–97) policy to encourage people to think of themselves as consumers of health and social care services. The national consumer organisations have extended their interests from the commercial marketplace to the public health and care services, so there are now *Which?* reports on health and social care topics and similar reports from the Scottish Consumer Council (Scottish Consumer Council and Scottish Association of Health Councils, 1992). Some health and care pressure groups have remodelled themselves on consumer organisations dealing with commercial products. The extract overleaf shows you one of these in the form of the recruitment advertisement for the Patients Association, a consumer organisation for the patients of the NHS. It publishes a newspaper featuring patient complaints and advice about complaining, a very clear guide on how to make complaints (Hogg, 1996), and supports patients and relatives in making them.

1991

Various aspects of government policy have clarified what service users have a right to expect from services. Initiatives here include the Patient's Charter which you considered earlier and the community care charters covering local authority social care. If you look back to the box on accountability structures in Section 1.2 you will see that the first item listed refers to statements about responsibilities. By clarifying what it is that service users have a right to expect, central government policy has automatically increased the accountability of services. In this sense the Patient's Charter gave the Patients Association a stick to beat the health service with. The fourth item listed for an accountability structure is about mechanisms for bringing individuals and agencies to account, and governments have required both health and social services to make their complaints procedures easier to understand and more easily available to service users (Scottish Office, 1991; Department of Health, 1991a, 1995c; Department of Health Social Services Inspectorate, 1994; National Health Service Executive, 1996a and b; Merry, 1996). The right of service users to be supported by advocates, whether during assessment or in making a complaint, has been written into much of the legislation of the 1980s and '90s. If the Woolfe reforms on civil law are implemented (Woolfe, 1996; Crail, 1996) it will be even easier for people to claim damages from health

<u>Your</u> Patients Association – We are here to listen CALL US WITH <u>YOUR</u> STORIES

We are here to make a difference for patients. We are here to listen, and then to respond. We are here to press for kinder, more accessible, more suitable, services which deliver better health outcomes for millions of individual people. What works for you is our focus. And you tell us that what you want is for health workers to ask you about the 'quality of life' issues that matter to you before you agree to treatment. We agree.

The PA seeks to listen to what people want to tell us. Our 'Patient-line' is the most essential part of all our work. You can call us for advice on [0181 423 8999].

• We <u>offer support</u>, guidance, contacts

• We <u>answer queries</u>, and help people find answers which will work for them.

• The PA puts your views to policy makers, to politicians and to government – <u>we make views heard where it counts.</u>

• We seek <u>to make desired changes actually happen</u>, by exercising influence and by working with managers – who want better services, and many of whose Health Authorities and NHS Trusts are members of the PA.

• The PA <u>campaigns for change</u>, and publicises your views widely in the media. We are called upon daily by the media for

authoritative guidance and comment.

• We are consulted at many levels, because we have a <u>distinctive voice</u>.

• The PA is open to all. It speaks up for necessary change, based on the evidence, experiences, stories and knowledge patients share with us.

It is evidence that we need to be able to call upon. By analysing what patients tell us we can increase our authority and influence. For this is indeed unique knowledge. Patients' stories of what happened to them must be applied to improving services.

(*Patients' Voices*, No. 1, Autumn 1996, p.1)

and social care services, although more often through mediation than through court proceedings.

 The reforms associated with the NHS and Community Care Act 1990 and its Northern Ireland equivalent have also fostered the development of assertive consumerism among service users. This is particularly so with regard to community care planning and locality commissioning (as described in Unit 18). The requirement that these activities are done through public consultation has given organised groups of service users the opportunity to question and influence the planning of services, although citizens' juries have the potential to cut them out. In many areas of the country service users are involved in setting the terms of contracts for those agencies which provide services, and in deciding how NHS trusts or providers of social care services should give an account of themselves in providing monitoring data to the service purchasers (as discussed in Unit 18). In addition, the contracting out of care services to voluntary sector agencies has, first, forced these agencies to be more accountable to those who provide their funds, as you glimpsed in the self-advocacy group example from Jan Wallcraft. And, second, it has given social and health services purchasers the opportunity to force voluntary sector agencies to make themselves more accountable to those who use their services.

The requirement to have a complaints procedure is a usual condition attached to a contract with health or social services, and there can be few publicly funded voluntary sector agencies today which do not have service user charters or something similar. This is often as a result of a requirement imposed upon them by the statutory agency with which they have a contract or service level agreement. On the whole, most voluntary sector organisations have welcomed this (Kumar, 1997).

Thus the development of assertive consumerism and the 1990s reforms of health and social services have developed together to make health and care agencies, and the individuals who work in them, more accountable to those who use the services. They may not be accountable enough in some people's view, and it might be argued that they are not accountable to the right people in the right ways, but they are much more accountable than they were before the 1990s.

2.2 Managerialism

At the same time that accountability to service users has increased, those who work in health and social care services have been made more accountable to their managers, and the agencies themselves have been made more accountable to central government directly, or more indirectly to regulatory bodies which carry out government policy and to inspecting bodies which investigate whether government policy is being implemented – as discussed earlier.

All of this puts pressure on the managers of health and social care services to direct the work of front-line workers more closely and make them more accountable for showing that they are actually following the procedures managers have laid down. This is one of the reasons for the large increase in record making discussed in Unit 19.

Management enthusiasm for this in the NHS is often enhanced by managers being paid on a performance-related basis, or having contracts which will not be renewed unless they meet specified performance targets.

The so-called 'new managerialism' in health and social services has sometimes been criticised as a device to limit expenditure. Up to a point this is true, but it has to be understood against a rise in real terms in expenditure on health and social services. What happened during the 1990s, at least until 1997/8, was that more treatments and more care packages were squeezed out of each billion pounds spent rather than there being any reduction in expenditure. The effect of this on the quality of care is another issue, and in this unit what is of interest is the effect on those who have had their accountability increased.

Key points

- Health, social and other public services have all been made more accountable during the 1990s. Two main, linked trends account for this:
  - the development of an assertive consumer movement among those who use health and social care services, facilitated greatly by the way the NHS and Community Care Act 1990 and its Northern Ireland equivalent provide opportunities for more public and service user involvement
  - the development of a 'new managerialism' making services much more accountable to central government, and thereby increasing the power of service managers over professionals and other staff.
- The 'contract culture' has had a similar effect, making voluntary and private sector providers more accountable to the managers in the agencies which purchase services from them.

MPs call for new targets for continence care

New national targets for continence care are being demanded by MPs amid claims
that standards are too low

23 March 1995

A top police officer has joined social workers in calling for
national standards to govern service for children in abuse
cases facing the courts

12 May 1995

NHS Responsibilities for meeting continuing care needs
sets out a range of services which health authorities, and
where appropriate GP fundholders, must provide. But
concern remains that a set of national eligibility criteria for
continuing health care has not been drawn up

29 June 1995

A campaign group including social services directors and charities
is calling for national standards to regulate continuing care …

29 June 1995

Labour has called for a shake-up of local government watchdog the Audit
Commission to refocus it on raising standards rather than simply bearing
down on costs [and] suggests that local authorities produce an annual
community care plan setting performance targets for services.

2 February 1996

The residential child care support task force this week repeated
its backing for mandatory child service plans

2 February 1996

*Accountability breeds accountability. The more people know about what happens in services, the more questions they
ask and the more information they demand. Hardly a week seems to go by without some demand for more precisely
defined standards, more monitoring or more regulation. (All quotations from* Care Weekly)

Section 3
What it's like to be accountable

When you know what your responsibilities are, and can carry them out, then being accountable can be a very satisfying state of affairs. Unfortunately, sometimes people don't know what they are responsible for, or, if they do, are not given the means to achieve it. Agencies often complain that they simply don't have enough resources to meet the performance targets set for them (e.g. Association of Metropolitan Authorities, 1993). This is investigated through the activities and case studies in this section.

The activities in this section involve using a questionnaire which is provided as Offprint 30. The situation of Usha Ayer, whom you met in Unit 18, will be used to familiarise you with the questionnaire. You will see that it is based on the items which appear in the box on 'structures of accountability' in Section 1.2 of this unit.

3.1 The case of Usha

The real Usha

The two people on whom the fictional character of Usha was based both perceived themselves to have acute problems of accountability. They didn't know who they were accountable to or what they were accountable for. They were both occupying posts funded by statutory services, but placed in the voluntary sector. In one respect they had a very clear job description. It told them to facilitate the development of new voluntary sector initiatives in the social care field. But their job descriptions didn't tell them which potential initiatives to choose, or how to choose between the many groups who had good ideas for development and who felt that these workers had been provided particularly for them. Management within the voluntary sector couldn't help them with this, since their management committees were made up of people with competing interests (for example, see Figure 2 in Unit 18 which shows the members of Usha's management committee). Managers in the statutory services were inhibited from instructing them in case this looked like the statutory sector trying to dictate to the voluntary sector.

 Now look at the questionnaire (Offprint 30). If these workers had been asked to fill it in they would probably have ticked 1(a), 1(b) and 1(c). They would probably have ticked 1(c) because they couldn't possibly achieve all that the various groups they met expected of them. As one of them said:

> *When it comes down to it, the job turned out to be picking winners, and that made the losers unhappy, the people who I couldn't give my attention to, and really no one ever gave me any guidance on who ought to have been winning; whether I made the right choices. All I know is that I got a lot of flack from people who felt let down and neglected, and they were often sitting opposite me in some meeting or other. I don't think I should have been given the power to decide, to help to decide, who was going to get funded.*

They would probably have also ticked 2(a) and 2(b), but perhaps with some hesitation, because they felt they should be providing evidence, but weren't at all sure what or to whom or in what way. For section 3 of the questionnaire, they felt that they were at risk of being sanctioned for doing things they were not in a position to do (b). They certainly got adverse criticism for favouring some groups and not others. The Asian woman felt there were unrealistic expectations (from the social services department) for her to work successfully with the local Urdu-speaking community, although she was of Indian background and a Hindu and they were Muslims, mainly from Kashmir, emotionally involved with Kashmir's campaign for independence from India. However, since there were no performance targets for these jobs, there could hardly be any severe penalties for failing to meet them, except non-renewal of contract. But that might have happened anyway, irrespective of how well they performed. Neither of these workers would have had anything to say about section 4 of the questionnaire, since there were no formal systems for bringing them to account unless they committed some serious disciplinary offence – and they didn't. And for section 5 they would probably have ticked (b), for reasons already explained. But since there were no formal systems for bringing them to account, it wouldn't have been at all clear whether they had been treated unjustly or not. Indeed, they probably wouldn't have known who had been saying what about them.

These jobs might seem to have given people the freedom to do what they wanted. In practice, whatever they did pleased some people and disappointed others, leaving them with a feeling of having let these others down. They experienced freedom as not knowing what they ought to be doing.

Now you are familiar with the questionnaire you can try it out for yourself.

Activity 5

Allow about 15 minutes

Your problems of accountability

You will need Offprint 30 for this activity.

Retrieve your notes from Activity 2, where you considered some form of accountability you had experienced yourself. Then using this as an *aide-mémoire* tick whichever of the boxes in the *first column* of the questionnaire seem best to describe the situation you noted down previously. You can tick more than one box in each numbered block if that is appropriate. There won't be any comment on this activity, but the remainder of the section includes case study material which you can compare with your own response.

3.2 The case of Michael

Michael
Michael (not his real name) was employed as a care assistant in a private sector nursing home specialising in older clients with dementia. If these people were reluctant to go where the staff wanted them to, or if they wandered disruptively or were aggressive to other residents, it was common practice for staff to use physical means to

restrain them or redirect them: for example by placing both hands on their shoulders and turning them around. Since the residents were frail relatively little force was required, but since they were frail even relatively little force might result in bruising or fracture. None of the care assistants appear to have had any training in this regard.

On one occasion a resident was poking another with a stick. Michael pulled her shoulder. Because of her osteoporosis this resulted in a fracture of the shoulder joint and the resident subsequently died of trauma. Michael reported what had happened to the proprietor, but the written report was made by the proprietor.

At the inquest Michael gave his account of the incident, but the care home proprietor read a written incident report which suggested that Michael had lost his temper with the resident. The coroner referred the case to the Crown Prosecution Service, but the CPS subsequently dropped it and the coroner returned a verdict of death by misadventure. The resident's relatives prepared a civil action against the nursing home. The civil action was dropped on legal advice when the nursing home proprietor showed he could demonstrate that the home had a written operational policy which forbade the use of physical restraint, claimed that Michael had been disobeying management guidance in this regard, and recited the incriminating incident report. Michael claimed that he had never seen the policy and that he had been misrepresented in the report. Michael was dismissed.

The local social services and health authority inspectors investigated the case, but did not withdraw registration. They were satisfied that the home had dismissed an unsuitable employee and in their report noted that the proprietor was putting an improved training scheme for care assistants into operation.

Activity 6 **Michael's accountability problem**

Allow about 5 minutes

Use the *second column* of boxes in the questionnaire to characterise Michael's accountability problem as shown in the case study box. You can believe his version of events for the purpose of this activity.

Comment

You probably ticked 1(a), insofar as Michael had not been given adequate instruction as to what the proprietor said was the home's policy on physical restraint, 2(a) insofar as it wasn't Michael who created the documentary evidence which counted, and especially 3(b), insofar as Michael was punished for doing something when he had not been given the instruction or the skill to do otherwise.

One of the interesting features of this case is the way it illustrates the allocation of blame between, on the one hand, an employee and, on the other, an organisation. Although in this case the organisation was actually the proprietor, in others it might be the management committee of a voluntary sector residential home, or the social services department in the case of a local authority home. In a broad sense, health and social care organisations are accountable for the safety and welfare of their clients (and their staff too): they have a legal *duty of care*. But how far this corporate responsibility extends depends on the legal concept of *vicarious liability*. Roughly speaking, organisations are not held responsible for damage done by their employees which they could not reasonably predict or could not feasibly prevent. You will see that the term 'reasonable' appears in this formula, and terms like 'reasonable', 'appropriate' and 'suitable' appear throughout the Registered Homes Act 1984, and other health and care legislation too. What was *reasonable* under the circumstances (and what the circumstances really were) is difficult enough to decide, but to make matters more difficult, coroners, the criminal law, the civil law and inspection teams may well have different ideas about what would have been reasonable.

Activity 7   **Who cops the blame?**

Allow about 20 minutes   Some coloured pencils or highlighters will help with this activity since it asks you to trace routes through the maze of Figure 2. Use the case study of Michael to inspect the figure. The end point of the case was the sequence 12, 13, 16. Michael took all the blame for the incident. He was neither prosecuted nor sued for damages, but he was sacked and he will probably never work in care again.

(a)   Work your way back from point 12 to the beginning of the figure. Remember that it is not what really happened in the home which is important, but whose version gets believed. Through what route was point 12 reached in this case?

(b)   Now look at the figure from Michael's point of view. Suppose he was in a position to take his employer to an industrial tribunal for unfair dismissal. How would he want the questions in the figure to be answered and where would he want the pathways to lead?

(c)   Now consider the resident's relatives. They decided not to sue Michael for damages, a very sensible decision given that Michael hadn't much money. But the care home proprietor was richer, was insured against such risks and had a legal duty of care, and there is a strong case for saying that he was negligent in this case. The relatives' case against the care home will be strengthened if they can demonstrate that the injury occurred because of organisational failings rather than because of individual malpractice. What route through the figure would their legal adviser try to achieve?

Comment   (a)   The actual route was 1, 3, 8, 12.

(b)   The route Michael might have preferred was 1, 3, 4, 6, 9, 13, 15 or 16. Ending at 15 might have strengthened his case since 16 leaves no one to blame in this case. But if he wanted reinstatement to his job, then 16 would have been preferable.

(c)   For the relatives 1, 2 and 14 would be the best route, but failing that 1, 3, 4, 6, 9, 13 and 15. The sequence 1, 3, 8, 12, 13 and 15 makes a less compelling case from the relatives' point of view since suggesting that Michael committed a criminal offence also implies he is the kind of person an employer could not reasonably be expected to control. Of course, if it could be proved that Michael already had a criminal record or history of violence, and the proprietor employed him knowing this, that would be a different matter.

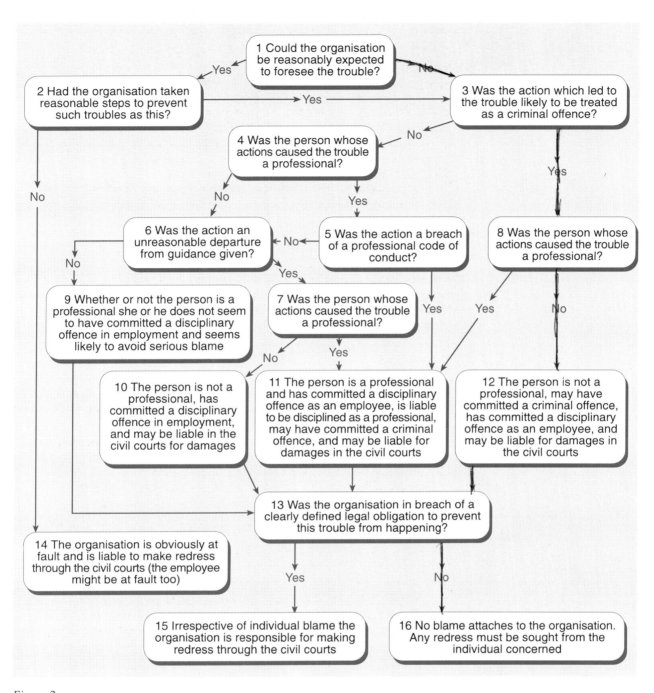

Figure 2
Considerations in deciding whether an employee or an employing organisation is at fault

There are three reasons why you were asked to do this activity. The first was to demonstrate what a tricky matter it can be to allocate blame between individuals and organisations. Both are accountable, but how each is brought to account and with what outcome depends very much on the actions of those who call them to account. In this case that means the actions of the doctor (who refused to sign the death certificate, thus provoking an inquest). Then there were the actions of the coroner, the police, the Crown Prosecution Service, the relatives and their legal advisers, the inspection team and, potentially, Michael bringing his employer to account for unfair dismissal and/or reporting him for perjury. This is highly characteristic of accountability in general. It is not something which is necessarily ever-present and which operates in a systematic way. Often whether people are brought to account, and for what and with what outcomes, is a very haphazard matter, as in this case.

Second, the case illustrates multiple systems of accountability characteristic of the health and care services. Workers are accountable:

- as individuals vulnerable to blame
- as members of organisations, making their agency blameworthy
- as employees and as employers in terms of employment law
- as citizens under criminal law
- to clients and their relatives in terms of contracts and/or the civil law
- to inspection units and regulatory bodies.

Although this didn't happen in the case study, the relatives might have held the inspection unit to account in various ways for its benign report on the home. If the resident's fees had been paid by social services they might have held the department accountable for placing their relative in an unsafe environment. Figure 2 also refers to professional accountability and that will be dealt with later.

Third, the case demonstrates the importance of documentary evidence in deciding such matters. There wasn't much, and what there was may have been falsified or misrepresented, but it still counted. The sources for this case study are Michael himself and a news cutting reporting the coroner's hearing. There can be no certainty as to whether Michael's account was accurate, but in reading the case your sympathies were probably with him rather than the proprietor, because it was his views which were put into a documentary form here. This links this unit with Unit 19, which discusses the connection between record making and accountability.

Activity 8   **Getting it on the record**

Allow about 10 minutes   (This activity is taken directly from an NHS training pack on record keeping.)

> *Mr Henry Shaw, 42, a multiple sclerosis patient, was admitted from a nursing home to a local community hospital with a chest infection. Staff on the ward observed, on admission, a small black area on his left buttock. During the stay the sore broke down and treatment was given according to the ward's pressure sore standards and documented in his notes. His chest improved and he was ready for discharge after seven days. Three days after discharge, the GP visited Mr Shaw in the nursing home. Mr Shaw told him that he now had a pressure sore which had developed in hospital. The GP complained to the Chief Executive and on investigation it was found that no written documentation concerning the blackened area had been made on admission.*
>
> *(a)   How could the nursing staff on duty support their argument that the sore was present on admission?*
>
> *(b)   Do you think the nurses are guilty of failure to keep essential records?*
>
> *(c)   Should the nursing home have informed the ward of the area on admission?*
>
> *(National Health Service Training Directorate, 1993, p. F3)*

Comment   The answers below are also taken directly from the NHS training materials, so they have a kind of official status.

> *(a)   As nothing was documented on admission, it would be difficult to prove that the sore was present at that time.*
>
> *(b)   Yes, for assessment purposes. Hopefully the progress report on treatment for the pressure sore during the seven day stay [was] accurate.*
>
> *(c)   Yes, but it is the nursing staff's responsibility to carry out an assessment initially on admission.*
>
> *(p. F18)*

It is important to note that this case has rather little to do with the quality of care provided for Mr Shaw on the ward, and much more to do with the quality of documentation in terms of which these nurses (mis)managed their accountability.

The same training pack notes that:

> *In 1992/93 more than a third of the complaints [in the NHS] which were upheld involved the lack of, or incorrect, information, i.e. poor record keeping. Often the problem isn't writing down the wrong thing, but not writing down anything at all.*
>
> *(p. B9)*

and quotes a solicitor specialising in NHS legal work as saying, 'If a plaintiff sees bad records, they are more likely to sue – they think 'shoddy records – shoddy care' (p. B10).

Key points

- Organisations are usually only legally responsible for problems which they could reasonably have been expected to predict and which they could have prevented by taking measures reasonable for them to take. But just what 'reasonable' means often has to be decided in court.

- People who work in health and social care contexts are usually involved in multiple structures of accountability. Which structure will come into play is often unpredictable.

- The investigation of records often determines who exactly was to blame, but that depends on what records there were to serve as evidence, and who made them.

3.3 Professional accountability

Michael did not belong to one of the professional occupations for which practitioners' names are listed on a register licensing them to practise. Therefore he could not be 'struck off' for failing to follow a professional code of practice or for having committed a criminal offence. Doctors, nurses, dentists and members of the professions allied to medicine (PAMs) such as occupational therapists, physiotherapists and chiropodists have this additional type of accountability. Since doctors, nurses and dentists cannot pursue their occupation at all if they have been struck off, and deregistered PAMs cannot be employed in the statutory services, this is a very serious kind of accountability. Had the proprietor of the home been a registered nurse, he might have found himself before the disciplinary committee of the United Kingdom Central Council for Nurses, Midwives and Health Visitors. He might have been found guilty of a professional offence irrespective of what happened in the criminal or the civil courts, and he might have been struck off the register. Struck off, he could still have been a nursing home proprietor, but if he counted himself as part of the complement of registered nurses a nursing home has to have, he could not have acted in that capacity.

The next case study does feature professionals and professional accountability as well as accountability as employees of NHS trusts. It is about hospital nurses. Unlike Michael, those nurses seem to spend a great deal of time writing things down.

Activity 9   **Accountability and risk**

Allow about 20 minutes

For this activity turn to Chapter 31 in the Reader, by Ellen Annandale. It is an extract from a longer article of the same title (Annandale, 1996). Read the article, ticking the *third column* of the questionnaire (Offprint 30) appropriately as if you were answering for the nurses interviewed. In the course of your reading look out for what Annandale says about the discrepancy between these nurses' perceptions of risk and the reality of risk.

Comment   For the questionnaire you probably ticked 1(c), 2(c), 3(b), 3(c), 4(c) and 5(b). The overall impression is of a group of workers who feel oppressed and vulnerable to being the subject of complaints. These might be justifiable from the patients' point of view but from the nurses' view they would be more properly directed at the government, trust management, or sometimes at doctors rather than at nurses, because in the nurses' view they have been given responsibilities without being given adequate means to discharge them. You might have noted that one box which these nurses would certainly not tick would be 1(a). If anything, their responsibilities are all too clearly defined and the problem is that they feel they cannot do what they are regarded as being responsible for doing.

Annandale's comments on the reality and the perception of risk are interesting. Nurses make up the largest single category of employees in the NHS but they are only rarely the subject of formal complaints by patients and relatives. Data on complaints are not collated nationally, so it is difficult to be precise about figures. Moreover, whom a complaint is directed at and who it is decided is at fault are often different matters. However, it is estimated (Institute for Health Services Management, 1993) that 80 per cent of complaints are about administration and catering and only 20 per cent of complaints are about treatment and care. The vast majority of these concern doctors.

It may be that fewer than 5 per cent of all formal complaints from patients and relatives are directed at nurses. Nurses are the subject of litigation in court only very rarely indeed (Annandale, 1996). The overwhelming majority of court cases involve doctors, directly or indirectly through a suit against a trust. But even a low rate of complaints against such a large group of workers generates enough news and gossip to worry the nurses. In fact, the most serious risk to nursing careers – although still a small one – comes from the

disciplinary procedures of the nursing profession itself, and a very large proportion of these cases result from one nurse, as a manager, reporting another, as a subordinate, for professional misconduct. While the idea of professionalism suggests the autonomy for individual practitioners to exercise their discretion, in practice professionalism in nursing is often used as a means through which one group of nurses, as managers, regulates and restricts another group of nurses, as employees (Kellet, 1996).

3.4 Responsibilities without the means to discharge them

Feeling that you are accountable for doing what you don't think you can possibly do seems to be a rather common feature of accountability in some areas of health and social care. Authorities often claim that they cannot meet performance targets or their legal obligations because they don't have enough resources. Annandale's nurses don't feel that they are given the resources or support necessary to avoid the need for patients to complain. She refers to 'patients as a source of risk', meaning that nurses risk patients complaining. But sometimes practitioners are at risk from their clientele in a different sense – service users are likely to do what practitioners are supposed to prevent them from doing but don't have the powers or the resources for prevention. The police, the probation service and social workers supervising young offenders often feel themselves unjustly criticised in this regard. The next activity examines this issue.

Activity 10   **The case of Liam**

Allow about 10 minutes   Liam (not his real name) is an approved social worker (he would be a mental health officer in Scotland, but Scottish mental health law is different). Under the terms of mental health legislation in England and Wales (Department of Health/Welsh Office, 1993) Liam has the power to recommend that someone should be compulsorily detained in hospital, if they are suffering from a mental disorder *and if* detention can be justified in the interests of:

- the person's health
- the person's safety
- the safety of other people.

The approved social worker's recommendation has to be supported by a doctor licensed to do so under the Mental Health Act 1983, usually a psychiatrist.

The social services department also has powers under Section 47 of the National Assistance Act 1948 to remove a person from insanitary living conditions and place them elsewhere against their will.

Now read the case study below and put yourself in Liam's position. What would you have done?

Liam

Mrs A was an older woman who caused considerable concern to her neighbours because she neglected herself and her property. Neighbours' concern resulted in one visit by the GP, two by the practice nurse and four by social workers over a period of three months. They were rarely admitted to the house and on each occasion Mrs A declined to accept any services offered. Liam was asked to visit. He gained entry to the house, which was sparsely furnished and cold, but relatively clean and with a proper water and electricity supply. Mrs A looked severely malnourished but was lucid and explained quite coherently that she didn't want other people interfering in her life.

Comment   Assuming you couldn't have been more persuasive than Liam, you might have considered the following.

1   It is doubtful whether conditions for using the provisions of the National Assistance Act obtained, since the house was not in an insanitary condition.

2   You might have considered initiating proceedings to have Mrs A committed to hospital under the terms of the Mental Health Act for assessment of her mental state, and to give her the benefits of hospital care. But Liam's powers depend on there being good evidence of mental illness and in his view she gave no indication of this.

3   You might have done nothing except to write a report indicating that the visit had been made, noting the circumstances found and your interpretation of these and, particularly, Mrs A's refusal of assistance.

What actually happened to Liam and Mrs A

In fact Liam took the last of the options described above. Some weeks later, following concern expressed by a neighbour, the police broke into Mrs A's house and found her dead. A coroner's inquiry found that she had died from self-neglect. The GP who gave evidence claimed 'it was obvious' that Mrs A was mentally ill and should have been committed to a psychiatric ward, and that she had originally referred the case to social services for this reason. The local newspapers ran headline stories about death by neglect on the part of social services, featuring interviews with the neighbours and the GP. Liam was suspended from duty on full pay, pending a confidential internal inquiry. He was completely exonerated since his actions were entirely consistent with mental health law, which is written precisely to make it difficult to undermine people's civil liberties by committing them to hospital against their will (Gomm, 1997). However, exoneration came after an agonising wait of three months and a loss of three months' service to the department.

So for Liam Mrs A constituted an accountability risk. You will have seen how in this case there was a conflict between, on the one hand, expectations for a social worker to prevent harm to a client and, on the other, the client's rights to privacy and self-determination. There are various areas of social care in which this kind of tension arises. For example, they arise with patients with dementia who 'wander' and thus endanger themselves and disturb other people's comfort and privacy, leading practitioners (and informal carers) to consider locked doors, electronic tags and worse. And they arise where social workers or health visitors are accused either of failing to detect and prevent child abuse, or alternatively of intruding unnecessarily into family life.

In Unit 19 you considered some very 'risky' people indeed: severely mentally ill people living in the community, such as Christopher Clunis. This case had an interesting development. In 1996, while the wife of Jonathan Zito was bringing a case for damages against Clunis for killing her husband, Clunis issued a writ against Camden and Islington Health Authority for negligence on the grounds that if the authority had given him appropriate treatment he would not have killed Jonathan Zito. He also claimed that the killing had caused his condition to worsen such that he is now unlikely to recover, and that as the result of his conviction he is unlikely to be released into the community during his lifetime. In December 1996 the health authority made a plea to the High Court to disallow Clunis's case on the grounds that if it succeeded he would be benefiting from a criminal act committed by himself. The High Court rejected this and the health authority appealed against the decision. In December 1997 the Court of Appeal disallowed Clunis's case. Clunis had asked the courts for indemnity against the case brought by Jane Zito on the grounds that the killing occurred because of the negligence of the health authority, and through no fault of his own. In another case, in July 1995, on legal advice, Leicestershire Health Authority made an out-of-court settlement of £30,000 to David Hoare, who had stabbed and killed a stranger, and had raised a case against the authority claiming that its negligence had led to the killing and caused him to suffer the consequences (Wilder, 1997).

Note that both of these cases were against the health authority and not against the NHS trusts responsible for delivering care. Health purchasers are legally responsible for what they purchase, but have very little capacity to influence the fine detail of health care. Clunis or Hoare might have sued the trusts instead or in addition, or individual practitioners and the health authorities might have sued the trusts to reclaim any money paid out in damages. Even when health authorities win such cases they are very costly since the health authority usually has to bear the costs of the litigation, which can run into hundreds of thousands of pounds (Wilder, 1997).

One of the difficulties in these kinds of cases is deciding responsibility in the most fundamental way. By some legal definitions, sometimes people who are severely mentally ill are not legally responsible for their actions. If they are not responsible for their own actions, there is a case for saying that someone else is accountable for what they do: hence there is a case for negligence against those authorities with a duty of care towards them when they kill or injure themselves or others. The law, however, is uncertain about this point. Practitioners faced with a situation like this would be likely to tick 1(c), 3(b), 3(c) and 5(b) on the questionnaire.

Key points

- Some agencies and workers in health and social care feel oppressed because they believe that they are highly accountable but unable to fulfil their responsibilities because:
  - they don't have the necessary resources
  - working arrangements make it impossible
  - they don't have the legal powers
  - it would be an unethical infringement of civil liberties.

- Some workers in health and social care find themselves held accountable for actions of service users which they cannot practically or legally prevent.

Section 4
Responding to accountability

So far this unit has drawn attention to the difficulties some agencies and some workers in health and social care experience through being made accountable. So how do they respond to this? One kind of response is often called 'defensive practice'.

4.1 Defensive practice

The term 'defensive practice' is often used to refer to tactics employed by practitioners when at risk of being judged adversely. The best defensive practice is to do your job so well that no one has reason to complain about it, although the term 'defensive practice' is rarely used to mean that. The news cutting overleaf suggests that the increased tendency of people to complain about general practitioners has actually improved their practice in some respects.

Activity 11 | **Positive and negative features of defensive practice**

Allow about 15 minutes | After reading the news cutting, which refers to research by Nicholas Summerton (1995), make two lists, one showing the benefits to patients of defensive practice, and the other the disadvantages to patients. This might not be as easy as it sounds.

Comment

Benefits to patients	**Disadvantages to patients**
More detailed note taking	More time on recording, less on treatment
More and better explanations to patients	Unnecessary prescriptions
More necessary diagnostic tests; risks justified by necessity for the tests	More unnecessary diagnostic tests with associated risks to patients
More necessary follow-ups	More unnecessary follow-ups
More necessary referrals	More unnecessary referrals
Less likely to do risky treatments in surgery	More likely to hospitalise patients who might safely have been treated in surgery
Practice audits	Striking off patients likely to complain or with difficult-to-treat conditions
	Much more costly practice

If your response is like the lists above, you will have realised that generalisations about whether these practices are beneficial or not won't necessarily apply to each and every patient. Thus, what might seem like an 'unnecessary' referral or an 'unnecessary' diagnostic test might in particular cases turn out to have been necessary, and what might seem like a procedure simple enough to carry out in the health centre might turn out to be very risky. This relates to another problem of accountability. Practitioners are accountable for assessing risks or assessing the benefits of treatment in advance, but only later know what the risks and benefits really were.

Defensive GPs 'help patients'

Chris Mihill Medical Correspondent

Doctors who carry out extra tests on patients in case they are sued may be giving the public a better service than those who do not, a researcher says today.

There has been concern about the alleged growth in Britain of 'defensive medicine' – whereby doctors carry out extensive and sometimes unnecessary tests to guard themselves against possible litigation – on the grounds that this wastes health service money and exposes patients to needless procedures.

But in a new survey, Nicholas Summerton, of Bradford Health Authority's department of public health medicine, says defensive medicine – particularly the more detailed explanation of what is to be done and more extensive note-taking of symptoms – can benefit patients.

Dr Summerton asked 300 general practitioners whether they had changed the way they worked for fear of complaints or legal action. Ninety-eight per cent said that they had made some practice changes in case a patient complained.

Around 60 per cent of the doctors said they were offering more diagnostic testing, more referrals to hospital, increased follow-ups and more detailed explanations. Some 40 per cent said they would avoid treating certain conditions in the surgery, and a similar proportion said they would consider extra diagnostic tests even where there was some risk to the patient.

Nearly 30 per cent said they would consider prescribing unnecessary drugs and 25 per cent said that they would remove patients from their list if they felt such patients were likely to complain.

Nine out of 10 of the doctors said they took more detailed notes and gave patients more detailed explanations, and a third said that they did more screening work or undertook practice audits to improve what they were doing.

Half the doctors said they were sometimes worried about being sued, and for 30 per cent this was a frequent worry. Just over 50 per cent said they were worried about a complaint being lodged with the family health services authority.

Dr Summerton, publishing the study in the British Medical Journal, says: 'Some defensive practices, such as more detailed note-taking, are clearly beneficial, but others will have adverse effects on both patient care and resource allocation.

'The existence of negative defensive medicine is perhaps best viewed as a symptom of the fundamental problems inherent within the present regulatory systems.'

Dr Summerton says that proposed changes to the complaints system will lead to an increase in complaints, and a corresponding rise in defensive practices which will not benefit patients.

(*Guardian*, 7 January 1995)

"It's not the risk to you I'm worried about. It's the risk to my career that bothers me."

Not all practitioners are in a position to respond to increased accountability by doing their job better, or by doing it in a way which is more pleasing to those to whom they are accountable. Then defensive practice can become a serious problem.

The range of tactics includes the following.

- Practitioners give as few undertakings as possible, make few promises, do not give service users predictions of what might happen, withhold from service users information about what they have a right to expect – on the grounds that the less they promise, the less people will complain about.

- They do not inform service users of their rights to complain, or they make complaining difficult. In the case of some GPs featured in the news cutting, they get rid of patients most likely to complain (Patients Association, 1996).

- They make records in such a way as to show that correct procedures were followed, even if they were not. Falsified records are quite common in negligence claims, compounding the offence if this is discovered.

- They make very extensive records just in case they are needed to rebut some accusation which is unpredictable at the time. Annandale's nurses employed this tactic.

- They practise out of sight of colleagues, superiors, or others who might give testimony to poor practice. The care assistants in the Reader chapter by Lee-Treweek, 'Bedroom abuse', are an example (Units 4 and 8).

- They practise in a way that limits the opportunities for service users to do anything a practitioner might get blamed for; in effect, they practise more coercively. After swinging in favour of more autonomy for mental health service users, the pendulum may now be swinging back the other way (Gomm, 1997).

As suggested in this unit, the first two of these tactics were more characteristic of health and social care up to the 1990s. They became rather more difficult to follow in the 1990s, so practitioners may be thrown back on the following tactics.

- They do things which are unnecessary but which, if not done, might lead to a complaint. This is often used as an explanation for why so many operations are performed in the USA, where patients are very ready to sue (Berliner, 1997). There were indications of this in the news cutting.

- They avoid doing something which might be beneficial but may be misunderstood or misrepresented. For example, many male primary school teachers or childcare workers avoid physical contact with the children they care for in the wake of public scandals about child abuse. Many first-aiders are now reluctant to assist at accidents given a spate of court cases against St John Ambulance and Red Cross volunteers.

- They never make a risky decision all by themselves. They always involve service users, colleagues and superiors in decision making. Then, if things go wrong, there will be a large number of people forced to support them (Tilley, 1996).

4.2 Bringing your employer to account

The defensive tactics listed above are often deployed when workers find themselves faced with impossible demands or fear unjust criticism. Think of the situation under which the care assistants practised in Chapter 25 in the Reader, 'Bedroom abuse'. The final section of the questionnaire (Offprint 30) is about protection against unfair accusation. It raises the issue of how employees can bring their employers to account for treating them unfairly.

Membership of a union is important for employee protection. Unionisation in health and social care varies from the largely non-unionised field of residential homes to the powerful unions, or 'professional associations', of doctors and nurses such as the British Medical Association and the Royal College of Nurses. Employee associations of this kind all offer advice, mediation and, if necessary, legal services when individual members are in dispute with an employer. There have been two contrary trends in health and social care during the 1990s. On the one hand, the development of 'a market for care' has meant far more part-time, short-term contract workers, agency staff and bank nurses, and more care being practised in small, non-unionised workplaces; more workers with little protection, like Michael for example (Section 3.2). On the other hand, partly because of Britain's membership of the EU, and partly because of the development of law in the British courts, legal protection with regard to unfair dismissal, equal opportunities, and health and safety at work increased markedly during the 1990s (Ryley, 1996; Rose, 1996). The implementation of the Disability Discrimination Act 1995 adds to legal protection for employees (Doyal, 1996). There is now good legal precedent for suing employers for the damages caused by stress at work, insofar as the employing organisation is responsible for this (Downy, 1995). Taking an employer to an employment tribunal or to court is a last resort. The most important impact of the law here is in encouraging employers to behave in ways that prevent the need for this to happen.

Sometimes it is the way in which an employing organisation treats service users which causes concern to employees, as the case of Mr Barton shows.

Mr Barton
Mr Barton was an ambulance driver for Wandsworth Council. He felt that the inexperience and lack of training of some of the escorts was a serious risk to the safety of the patients. Managers promised action, but nothing was done. Frustrated with this, Mr Barton walked into his manager's office with a tape recorder to quiz her about the situation. He subsequently reported the council to the Health and Safety Executive and an inquiry by the Executive confirmed Mr Barton's views. Mr Barton was demoted and given a warning that he would be dismissed if he behaved in this way again within the next two years. He took this as a case of 'victimisation' to an employment tribunal. The tribunal found that Mr Barton had responded to a threat to safety which was 'serious and immediate' and that Mr Barton had taken 'appropriate steps to protect himself and others from danger'. He was found to have acted as he should have acted in terms of health and safety law. Mr Barton was reinstated and paid compensation. The problem of untrained escorts has been remedied. (Adapted from Rose, 1996, p. 10)

Activity 12   **From the escort's point of view**

Allow about 10 minutes   Read the case of Mr Barton, but from the viewpoint of an 'inexperienced', 'untrained' escort. Jot down your own ideas about whether you would feel supported by Mr Barton's action or threatened by it.

Comment   Your inexperience might cause an accident and you might be dismissed for this or perhaps even sued for damages. You would be in the same situation as Michael (Section 3.2). You would probably welcome training. You might feel differently if you risked being sacked and replaced by someone more experienced – but would you really be happy about continuing in work that put you in a situation of such risk?

As Mr Barton's case shows, bringing your own employer publicly to account for bad practice can be occupationally damaging and unpleasant. Legal changes recently have made it safer to do but it is not to be recommended without the advice and support of a trade union or professional association, and/or of Public Concern at Work, the organisation for 'whistle-blowers'. However, when matters like this go to litigation, it is usually evidence of a badly managed organisation which is unwilling to learn from the experience of its employees. Not all organisations in health and social care are like this. It is usually possible for employees to remind their employers of their legal obligations, to draw attention to bad practice and to hazards, without risking a career. As Burke and Dalrymple (1996) point out, the law regarding the entitlements of service users is a facility which can be used by employees against employers in favour of service users, and usually without risking sanctions (see also Cragg, 1995). It is not uncommon for practitioners to encourage aggrieved service users to make complaints about a service, and indeed under the new complaints procedures

(Section 2.1) they are supposed to make it easy for service users to make complaints. Moreover, given the dispersion of health and social care across a large number of agencies, it is sometimes possible to bring someone else's employer to account. Many formal complaints about social services from service users have the informal support of a doctor or nurse, and many complaints from patients about health services have the encouragement of a social worker.

4.3 Effective accountability structures

So far this unit has drawn your attention to a great many problems relating to accountability, so perhaps you are beginning to feel that such problems might be resolved by making practitioners or agencies *less* accountable.

Activity 13   **Unaccountability**

Allow about 5 minutes

First scan through the questionnaire (Offprint 30) again, then focus on responses 2(a), 3(a), 4(a) and 5(a). Anyone who ticked all these boxes would be describing their situation as one of unaccountability. For this activity think of the kinds of trouble which might arise where health and social care practitioners were completely autonomous in this regard. What kind of person would *you* allow to be unaccountable as a practitioner in health and social care contexts?

Comment   Probably if you were prepared to allow anyone at all to be unaccountable you would have to regard that person as enormously talented and trustworthy – saintly even! But in a sense this question contradicts itself. How would you know that someone had these characteristics in the first place, or continued to show them, without some means to make them accountable for their actions. In reality, of course, the issue is not one of choosing between accountability and unaccountability, but of deciding how much or how little to trust practitioners and agencies to act without making themselves accountable.

Accountability itself is not the problem. The problems of accountability arise from the way in which particular structures of accountability are organised. That is what you have been considering in this unit so far. The next box summarises this discussion in the form of a set of questions which might be asked of any organisation about the adequacy of its accountability structures.

Some questions to ask about accountability

- Are responsibilities clearly defined and do people have the wherewithal to discharge their responsibilities?

- Is accountability to the right body of people and, if accountability is to several different stakeholder groups, are there mechanisms for reaching agreements between them so that staff do not face being pulled in different directions?

- Is the appropriate evidence of performance generated and without incurring so much effort that it prevents the achievement of something more worthwhile?

- Are there opportunities to learn from what goes wrong, rather than resorting to blame and punishment or litigation, and, if sanctions are necessary, are they proportionate to the harm done? Are there rewards for good performance as well as punishments for bad?

- Is there adequate protection for staff against unjust accusation which is not so watertight that it makes them invulnerable to legitimate complaint?

For the cases you have considered in this unit some of the answers were 'no'. You saw what kinds of trouble that caused. But when any of the answers are 'no' there is rarely much that front-line practitioners can do about it individually. They might improve matters by acting together to influence their managers or make alliances with service user groups to the same end. But some of the problems of accountability experienced by staff are deeply rooted in the structure of health and social services. They are shaped by national legislation. Some relate to shortages of resources on the one hand, as against, on the other, the unrealistic expectations of services users, governments, the public and the media.

Conclusion

There were four core questions for this unit. The first of these was:

• What does it mean to be accountable?

Section 1 explained the notion of accountability. It looked at the various directions in which people could be accountable and the various mechanisms used to bring them to account. As was noted there, being accountable means having your autonomy restricted and this has been a particular concern for professionals, who have always prized their 'professional autonomy'. Professional autonomy is discussed further in Block 7.

Section 3 also indicated that sometimes being accountable means being in a very uncomfortable position, if you are accountable for doing something which circumstances do not permit, or vulnerable to blame for what you could not have avoided.

The second question was:

• Why has there been pressure to increase the level of accountability in health and social care?

Section 2 answered this question in terms of the development of assertive consumerism among those who use health and care services. The self-advocacy groups you met in Unit 18 are good examples of this. And Section 2 also answered this question in terms of the increase in central government control over local health and social services, manifesting itself in increased managerial control over practitioners in health and social care. In addition, the traditional autonomy of voluntary sector agencies has been reduced through contracting their services to the statutory authorities. This is because the statutory authorities remain accountable for the services they contract and therefore may impose strict conditions on contractors in order to discharge their own duty of care through these other organisations.

There was a considerable tightening up of accountability during the 1990s, but in October 1997 people were still making strident demands for more. You read this in the article by McIver and Martin (Offprint 29); virtually every service user organisation has campaigned for services to be more accountable to service users, and it seems highly likely that they will go on doing so. Moreover, the debate about accountability has been part of a wider debate about the democratic control of health and social care services, and seems likely to continue to be so. During the 1980s the NHS ceased to have any element of local democratic control, while the real power of locally elected councils over social services was greatly diminished. In the 1990s elements of democratic control began to creep back in. But this was through the very haphazard process of locality planning, as discussed in Unit 18. At the end of the 1990s there seems to be a movement building for the more systematic, local democratic control of health and social care services (Stewart, 1995, 1997).

The broader background in which demands for more accountability have developed is discussed in Block 7 of this course.

The third core question was:

• What problems arise for people and agencies who are made accountable and how do they respond to these?

Sections 3 and 4 illustrated these kinds of problems with some case studies. You saw that problems of accountability arise when it is unclear what people's responsibilities are, when they have responsibilities they are not able to fulfil, and when they are accountable in one direction for doing one thing, and in another direction for doing the opposite. Reducing accountability was probably not an option in the late 1990s given the groundswell of support for increasing it at that time, nor probably would it be desirable. Of course, many practitioners could be relied upon if they were treated as trustworthy and allowed more autonomy. But without some system of accountability it is not easy to distinguish those who can be trusted from those who cannot.

Section 4 used the term 'defensive practice' to refer to the responses made by people in the face of difficult situations of accountability. As noted, some defensive practice is good practice insofar as it avoids complaint by giving people nothing to complain about and promotes the welfare of service users. But sometimes being 'over-accountable' to service users may mean doing what they want even if it does them harm. There is an ethical issue here about whose opinion should prevail in such circumstances: the service user's or the practitioner's. And sometimes defensive practice means wheeling and dealing, ducking and diving, to make sure that wherever the blame falls, it doesn't fall on you. When people are accountable for achieving what it is impossible for them to achieve, the latter is often their only defence.

The unit finished by reviewing the characteristics of accountability structures which would enable agencies and practitioners to be accountable to the right people, for achieving what they should and can achieve, to learn from mistakes, and to avoid unjust accusations.

That was the beginning of an answer to the last core question:

- How might accountability be organised to promote high-quality care?

In Block 6 you will be considering this question in terms of the structures of accountability needed to prevent the abuse of service users.

Study skills: Managing during the summer

Late July and August – what the newspapers call 'the silly season' – can be an awkward time for OU students. Many find it harder to concentrate on study when the evenings stay light and the weather outside is more inviting. And then school holidays and going away on holiday can cut right across normal patterns of life, throwing study plans into confusion. Also, the OU study centres close, leaving a gap in the tutorials; your tutor too may be unavailable for a spell. Yet your study programme continues.

K100 allows a two-week break to be taken at your convenience (probably during your study of Block 6). Block 6 is the usual four units in length, but the gap between TMA 05 and TMA 06 is six weeks. Of course, you don't *have* to take the break. You can keep right on and get to the end of the course with a couple more weeks for your exam preparations. Or you can use the two extra weeks to slow down and spread your work out, rather than have a complete break.

But even with the extra two weeks, if your summer arrangements are really disruptive you may still fall behind. If so, don't despair. Just work out the best solution you can. If necessary, you may have to cut some corners – not cover everything you might otherwise have done. Whatever happens, don't let yourself lose momentum, or lose heart, just because things get tricky for a few weeks. Having reached this far (past the two-thirds mark), you owe it to yourself to push on to the end of the course.

References

Annandale, E. (1996) 'Working on the front-line: risk culture and nursing in the new NHS', *Sociological Review*, Vol. 44, No. 3, pp. 416–51.

Association of Community Health Councils of England and Wales (1995) *Health Perspectives: the New Patient's Charter*, ACHCEW, London.

Association of Metropolitan Authorities (1993) *Mental Health Services: Issues for Local Government*, AMA, London.

Audit Commission (1995) *Local Authority Performance Indicators*, Vol. 1, Vol. 2 and Appendix to Volumes 1 and 2, Audit Commission, London.

Berliner, D. (1997) 'Law of averages', *Health Service Journal*, 20 March, pp. 30–31.

Boyal, S. and Darkins, A. (1994) 'Health care markets: abstract wisdom or practical nonsense?', in Harrison, A. and Bruscini, S. (eds) *Health Care UK 1993/94*, King's Fund Institute, London.

Brindle, D. (1995) 'The consultation cure', *Guardian*, 10 May, p. 7.

Brindle, D. (1997) 'Key court victory for child carers', *Guardian*, 1 February, p. 7.

Brochie, J. and Wann, M. (1993) *Training for Lay Participation in Health*, Patients Association, London.

Brown, C. and Dobson, R. (1997) 'Abuse checks on all foster parents', *Independent*, 24 May, p. 1.

Burke, B. and Dalrymple, J. (1996) 'Defensive weapon', *Community Care*, 4–10 July, p. 26.

Cambridge City Council (1996) *Performance Indicators 1995/6*, Cambridge City Council, Cambridge, p. 2.

Care Weekly (1995) 'Ombudsman attacks Lambeth in child case', 6 January, p. 3.

Charity Commissioners for England and Wales (1996) *Responsibilities of Trustees*, Charity Commission for England and Wales, London.

Combes, R. (1995) 'Caring league prompts point scoring fears', *Care Weekly*, 30 March, p. 1.

Cooper, L., Coote, A., Davies, A. and Jackson, C. (1995) *Voices Off: Tackling the Democratic Deficit in Health*, Institute for Public Policy Research, London.

Council for the Professions Supplementary to Medicine (1997) *Annual Report 1996–97*, Council for the Professions Supplementary to Medicine, London.

Cragg, S. (1995) 'Using the law to challenge community care decisions', *Mental Health Nursing*, Vol. 15, No. 3, pp. 7–8.

Crail, M. (1996) 'Keeping Woolfe from the door', *Health Service Journal*, 8 August, p. 12.

Department of Health (1991a) *The Right to Complain: Practice Guidance on Complaints Procedures in Social Services Departments*, HMSO, London.

Department of Health (1991b) *The Patient's Charter*, HMSO, London.

Department of Health (1992) *The Health of the Nation: A Strategy for Health in England*, HMSO, London.

Department of Health (1995a) *The Patient's Charter and You*, Department of Health, London.

Department of Health (1995b) *The Patient's Charter* (revised edn), HMSO, London.

Department of Health (1995c) *Acting on Complaints*, EL/95/36, Department of Health, London.

Department of Health (1996) *Coordinating Community Mental Health Care*, Department of Health/The Open University, Milton Keynes.

Department of Health and Social Services, Northern Ireland (1992) *A Regional Strategy for Northern Ireland 1992–97*, DHSSNI, Belfast.

Department of Health Social Services Inspectorate (1994) *Complaints Procedures in Local Authority Social Services Departments: Second Overview Report*, Chief Inspector's letter (94) 28, Department of Health, London.

Department of Health Social Services Inspectorate/Scottish Office Social Work Services Group (1991) *Care Management and Assessment: Practitioner's Guide*, HMSO, London/Edinburgh.

Department of Health/Welsh Office (1993) *Mental Health Act 1983: Code of Practice*, HMSO, London/Cardiff.

Downy, R. (1995) 'Stress takes its toll on childcare staff', *Community Care*, 1–7 June, pp. 4–5.

Doyal, B. (1996) *Disability Discrimination Act: The New Law*, Jordans, Bristol.

Eastern Health and Social Services Board (1995) *Setting Priority Standards for Social Work Practice*, EHSSB, Belfast.

Eaton, L. (1996) 'Safety in the homes', *Community Care*, 21–27 November, pp. 16–17.

General Medical Council (1993) *Professional Conduct and Discipline; Fitness to Practise*, GMC, London.

Gomm, R. (1997) 'Supervision Registers' and 'Community Supervision' in The Open University, K257 *Mental Health and Distress: Perspectives and Practice, Offprints Book*, pp. 68–72.

Gordon, R. (1993) *Community Care Assessments: A Practical Legal Framework*, Longman, Harlow.

Harris, J. (1996) 'Peace deals', *Health Service Journal*, 16 May, Special Law Report, pp. 1–5.

Health Promotion Wales/Hybu Iechyd Cymru (1990) *Health Promotion Challenges for the 1990s*, Health Promotion Wales/Hybu Iechyd Cymru, Cardiff.

Heginbotham, C. (1992) *Listening to Local Voices*, National Association of Health Authorities and Trusts, Birmingham.

Hogg, C. (1996) *How Do I Make a Complaint?*, Patients Association, London.

Institute for Health Services Management (1993) *How to Handle Complaints: Guidance on Good Practice in Dealing with Patient Complaints*, IHSM, London.

Kellet, J. (1996) 'A nurse suspended', *British Medical Journal*, Vol. 313, pp. 1249–50.

Kumar, S. (1997) *Accountability: Relationships Between the Voluntary Sector 'Providers', Local Government 'Purchasers' and Service Users in the Contract State*, Joseph Rowntree Foundation/York Publishing Services, York.

Local Government Management Board (1995) *Equalities in the Contract Culture: A Handbook*, Local Government Management Board, Luton.

McKechnie, S. (1996a) 'Community health councils' in Merry (1996) p. 255.

McKechnie, S. (1996b) 'Consumer groups', in Merry (1996) pp. 252–56.

Merry, P. (ed.) (1996) *1996–7 NHS Handbook* (11th edn), National Association of Health Authorities and Trusts/JMH Publishing, London.

Mihill, C. (1995) 'Defensive GPs "help patients"', *Guardian*, 7 January.

Muijen, M. (1995) 'Scare in the community: part five; care of mentally ill people', *Community Care*, supplement, 7–13 September, pp. i–viii.

National Association of Health Authorities and Trusts (1997) *A Measure of Effectiveness? A Critical Review of the NHS Efficiency Index*, NAHAT, Birmingham.

National Health Service Executive (1994) *The NHS Ethnic Health Unit*, EL(93)89, Department of Health, London.

National Health Service Executive (1996a) *Implementation of New Complaints Procedures*, EL(96)19, Department of Health, Leeds.

National Health Service Executive (1996b) *Complaints: Listening ... Acting ... Improving. Guidance on Implementation of the NHS Complaints Procedure*, Department of Health, Leeds.

National Health Service Management Executive (1992) *Local Voices: The Views of People in Purchasing Health Services*, NHSME, London.

National Health Service Management Executive (Scotland) (1997) *Primary Care: An Agenda for Action*, NHSME/Scottish Office, Edinburgh.

National Health Service Training Directorate (1993) *Just for the Record: A Guide to Record Keeping for Health Care Professionals*, NHSTD, Bristol.

National Opinion Polls (1994) *Development of the Patient's Charter Literature: Report on the Findings of a Qualitative Research Study*, National Opinion Polls, London.

Northern Ireland Office (1991) *Care Management: Guidance on Assessment and the Provision of Community Care*, Northern Ireland Office, Belfast.

Ogden, J. (1996) 'Open court', *Health Service Journal*, 9 May, pp. 12–13.

The Open University (1992) B789 *Managing Voluntary and Non-profit Enterprises*, The Open University, Milton Keynes.

The Open University (1996) K263 *Managing Roles and Relationships: Perspectives on Practice in Health and Welfare*, Workbook 4, *Roles in the System*, The Open University, Milton Keynes.

Patients Association (1996) 'Are you an expensive patient? Are you a 'nuisance'? Are you struck off? Can we help?', *Patients' Voice*, Autumn, p. 2.

Phillips, A. (1994) *Charitable Status: A Practical Handbook* (2nd edn), Interchange Books, London.

Public Law Project (1994) *Is It Lawful? A Guide to Judicial Reviews*, Public Law Project/Unison, London.

Rose, N. (1996) 'Worth the whistle', *Health Service Journal*, 16 May, Special Law Report, p. 10.

Ryley, M. (1996) 'Equal to the occasion', *Health Service Journal*, 16 May, Special Law Report, pp. 8–9.

Scottish Consumer Council/Scottish Association of Health Councils (1992) *Patients' Rights: GP and Hospital Services*, Scottish Consumer Council, Glasgow.

Scottish Office (1991) *Complaints Procedures*, SW5/91/, Home and Health Department, Scottish Office, Edinburgh.

Scottish Office (1992) *Scotland's Health: A Challenge To Us All – A Policy Statement*, HMSO, Edinburgh.

Stewart, J. (1995) *Innovation in Democratic Practice*, School of Public Policy, University of Birmingham.

Stewart, J. (1997) *Further Innovation in Democratic Practice*, School of Public Policy, University of Birmingham.

Summerton, N. (1995) 'Positive and negative features in defensive medicine: a questionnaire study of general practitioners', *British Medical Journal*, Vol. 310, pp. 27–9.

Tilley, J. (1996) 'Accounts, accounting and accountability in psychiatric nursing' in Watson, R. (ed.) *Accountability in Nursing Practice*, Chapman & Hall, London.

United Kingdom Central Council for Nursing, Midwifery and Health Visiting (1996a) *Issues Arising from Professional Conduct Complaints*, UKCC, London.

United Kingdom Central Council for Nursing, Midwifery and Health Visiting (1996b) *Guidelines for Professional Practice*, UKCC, London.

Wallcraft, J. (1993) 'Empowering empowerment: professionals and self-advocacy projects', *Journal of Mental Health Nursing*, Vol. 14, No. 2, pp. 7–9.

Whiteley, P. (1996) 'Newcastle MIND closed by funding crisis', *Community Care*, 8–14 February, p. 9.

Wilder, G. (1997) 'Pay-back time', *Health Service Journal*, 20 March, pp. 28–30.

Woolfe, Lord Chief Justice (1996) *Access to Justice: The Final Report* (Woolfe report), HMSO, London.

Acknowledgements

Grateful acknowledgement is made to the following sources for permission to reproduce material in this unit:

Text

'Ombudsman attacks Lambeth in child case', *Care Weekly*, No. 352, January 1995. Published by permission of the editor of *Community Care*; Brown, C. and Dobson, R. (1997) 'Abuse checks on all foster parents', *The Independent*, 24 May; Ogden, J. (1996) 'Open court', *Health Service Journal*, 9 May, © Joy Ogden 1996; Spiers, J. and Howland, G. (1996) 'Your patients association – We are here to listen, call us with your stories', *Patients' Voices*, No. 1, The Patients Association; Mihill, C. (1995) 'Defensive GPs "help patients"' *The Guardian*, 7 January, © Guardian Newspapers Ltd.

Illustrations/photographs

p. 137: Press Association; *p. 139*: Extract from *Cambridge City Council's Performance Indicators, 1995/96*, reproduced by kind permission of Cambridge City Council.

Unit 21
Confidentiality: Policy and Practice

Prepared for the course team by Roger Gomm

While you are working on Unit 21, you will need:
- Course Reader
- *The Good Study Guide*
- Media Notes
- Audio Cassette 5, side 2
- Wallchart
- Pathways VQ Guide

Contents

Introduction

Unit 21 focuses on:

- the duty of confidentiality
- how to put confidentiality policy into practice
- contributing to the development of agency policy and practice
- working with numbers – scatter diagrams
- preparing for the examination.

This is the fifth of the K100 skills units. The first of them (Unit 5) considered some of the principles which should underpin good practice in social and health care – the value base. As a reminder, these were:

1   enable people to develop their own potential

2   enable people to have a voice and be heard

3   respect people's beliefs and preferences

4   promote and support people's rights to appropriate services

5   respect people's privacy and rights to confidentiality.

This unit focuses on the last of these and deals with the duty of confidentiality and how to put it into practice.

This unit also continues the task of helping you to develop your study skills. In Section 5 you will find activities on numerical and graphical skills centred on reading scatter diagrams and activities on preparing for the examination.

Central themes of the unit

For all three units in this block so far the central topic has been information. Much of the information involved in health and social care refers to matters which service users would prefer not to be broadcast widely. Unit 19 included a great deal of material on privacy and confidentiality, and so does this one. However, the skills units of this course deal with topics in a more practical way, to help you recognise and develop the practical skills which are needed for competent work in health and social care. So in this unit you will be asked to make the kinds of decisions which people in health and social care really do make when they apply a confidentiality policy to the situations which arise in the course of their work.

Privacy and confidentiality always feature in the lists of values subscribed to by professional groups involved in health and social care – and by many others as well, such as lawyers, accountants and the clergy. The following box quotes the relevant clauses from the code of practice for nurses. Serious and unjustifiable breaches of confidentiality by professionals can lead to their being struck off the professional register.

The confidentiality of care for nurses

As a registered nurse, midwife or health visitor, you are personally accountable for your practice and, in the exercise of your professional accountability, must ...

10   protect all confidential information concerning patients and clients obtained in the course of professional practice and make disclosures only with consent, where required by the order of a court or where you can justify disclosure in the wider public interest;

(United Kingdom Council for Nurses, Midwives and Health Visitors (UKCC), 1992, clause 10)

(Guidance on how to apply the code is given in UKCC, 1996, paras 50–69.)

Confidentiality is also one of the fundamental values which is assessed in VQ schemes in health and social care. The next box quotes from the revised Level 3 in care as current in 1998, but care awards at other levels and in other fields also view confidentiality as an important principle.

Confidentiality in a VQ scheme

02.3   Promote people's right to the confidentiality of information
       Performance criteria
(1)   information stored in, and retrieved from, recording systems is consistent with the requirements of legislation and organisational policy
(2)   records made by the worker are accurate and legible and only contain the information necessary for the record's purpose
(3)   information is only disclosed to those who have the right and the need to know once proof of identity has been obtained
(4)   the appropriate precautions are taken when communicating confidential or sensitive information to those who have the right and need to know it
(5)   when someone tells the worker something which the worker is required to share with others, the person is clearly told in an appropriate manner that the information may need to be shared with others
(6)   confidential records are handled securely and stored in the correct place
(7)   support is sought by the worker when it appears that information is being misused.

(CCETSW/City and Guilds, 1997, p. 8)

(For more detail about the assessment of competence in VQ schemes see the Pathways VQ Guide for K100.)

All the practice skills activities in this unit ask you to interpret and apply a confidentiality policy which is provided for you to work with in Sections 1 and 2.

Some of the practice activities will be suitable for inclusion in a K100 portfolio. Unit 5 explained how such a portfolio might be produced and the uses to which it might be put. Section 4 will explain which of the Unit 21 activities are suitable for your portfolio. The same activities might be suitable for including in a portfolio for assessment according to National or Scottish Vocational Qualifications Standards. For further details about this see the K100 Pathways VQ Guide.

Section 1

Introducing an agency and its confidentiality policy

Nearly everyone who works in a health or social care context works in an organisation which has a written confidentiality policy and/or belongs to an occupational group which has its own code of practice. Such policies or codes don't answer all the questions. They are sometimes difficult to apply to particular circumstances. But they do reduce the number of occasions when workers find it difficult to know what to do. Because of such policies and codes, much confidentiality practice is a matter of following some printed rules. The skill then is in working out how the rules apply in particular situations.

Confidentiality policies quite rightly differ from agency to agency, because different agencies have a 'need to know' different kinds of information, and because different agencies are confronted with different challenges in trying to keep information confidential. Since the 'right answers' on confidentiality differ from agency to agency, it is necessary to give you a particular confidentiality policy to work with for this unit.

1.1   Narcotics Information and Advice Service

For the purpose of this unit you will be using a policy written for a fictional 'street' drug agency, which offers information and counselling to people who have problems with drugs: the Narcotics Information and Advice Service Ltd, or NIAS for short. The agency is fictional, but closely based on a number of real agencies of this kind. In fact the policy you are going to work with is based on that for the Chrysalis Project in East Hertfordshire, although the two policies are not identical; nor is Chrysalis quite like NIAS. The fictional agency, NIAS, is introduced in the box below.

Introducing the Narcotics Information and Advice Service Ltd

NIAS is a 'street' drug agency, meaning that people can refer themselves to it directly, by walking in through the door or by telephone. It also accepts referrals from the drug problem team (see below) or from GPs, social workers, health visitors, youth workers, teachers and other professionals, so long as the person concerned agrees to be dealt with by NIAS. The agency offers a range of services, including information about drugs, advice on how to use drugs more safely, and a needle and syringe exchange where drug users can return their used needles and pick up clean ones. It also offers support to people who want to give up drugs, and will help its clients to access or deal with other agencies, such as the housing department or another landlord, the Benefits Agency, the criminal justice system (police, probation, courts and lawyers), social services and GPs. It has a contract with social services for assessing clients' suitability for rehabilitation at residential rehabilitation centres (for which social services pay).

Staff at NIAS work closely with the drug problem team (DPT) in the local NHS trust, which is the main prescriber of methadone (the drug prescribed as a legal alternative to heroin). Not all NIAS clients are clients of the DPT, and not all DPT clients are in contact with NIAS. Workers at NIAS attend the weekly meetings of the DPT, where decisions are made on whether cases should be dealt with by NIAS, or by one of the community addiction nurses, or both. Matters discussed at the DPT meetings are covered by both the NIAS and the NHS trust confidentiality policies.

NIAS has seven permanent staff and a number of sessional workers. It has a team of volunteers who usually befriend one or more clients. It is a company limited by guarantee and a charity, and has an unpaid management committee elected at a public annual general meeting. Most of its funding comes from contracts with the health authority and the local authority social services department. Both scrutinised the NIAS confidentiality policy and checked it against their own criteria for contractors' confidentiality policies as a condition of awarding the contracts.

NIAS maintains two offices five days a week in two large towns and satellite offices one day a week each in two small market towns. The two full-time offices have an appointments-only system in the mornings, a drop-in service in the afternoons, and one late-night opening in each office. Workers and volunteers also visit people in their homes and in prison.

Activity 1 **Introducing NIAS**

Allow about 15 minutes Having read the sketch of the agency, jot down your initial thoughts about the kinds of information which might be 'sensitive', and which NIAS will be particularly concerned to keep confidential. There will be no comment to this activity since the activities which follow cover most of the more sensitive kinds of information.

1.2 The confidentiality policy

The next box gives the first 14 clauses of confidentiality policy for the agency. Read it through now, although you will need to keep referring back to it. The last six clauses of the policy are given in Section 2.

Confidentiality policy: NIAS (clauses 1–14)

1 **The responsibilities of employees/volunteers**

NIAS recognises that its clients have a right to have information about them kept confidential, and that this is essential for maintaining their trust in the agency and hence essential for running the service.

Following the policy stated in this document is:
* a condition of employment in the agency and breaches of it may lead to dismissal

- a condition of being a volunteer in this agency and breaches of it may lead to a volunteer being asked to leave.

These responsibilities persist even after a person has ceased to be an employee/volunteer with the agency.

2   **The scope of the policy**

- In this policy 'a client' is defined as anyone who approaches the agency for information, advice or any other service, whether as a user of drugs, or as someone concerned about another's drug use.
- The policy is binding on paid employees and volunteers including members of the management committee.

3   **Information obtained other than through work in the agency**

(i)   Confidential information obtained about clients by employees/volunteers in a capacity *other than as an employee/volunteer with the agency* (for example, by gossip or through work in another agency or about one client from another) should not enter the agency's information system, unless non-disclosure would pose a serious risk to health and safety.

(ii)   Information gained by gossip, hearsay, or by breach of confidentiality elsewhere should still be treated as confidential information. (See clauses 4 and 5.)

4   **Information obtained through the work of the agency**

Information obtained about a client through the work of the agency may be shared among employees/volunteers in the agency on a need-to-know basis and will only be disclosed outside the agency according to the conditions in clause 5.

5   **Transfers of information beyond the agency**

Information about clients will be transferred to people outside the agency only under the circumstances listed below. 'People' here includes other agencies, relatives and friends of the client, and relatives and friends of employees/ volunteers.

5a   With the client's explicit consent

(i)   Explicit consent should normally be given through the client signing a consent form. When it is necessary to act on a client's verbal consent (perhaps given by telephone) this should be followed up by the client signing a consent form as soon as possible thereafter.

(ii)   All reasonable efforts should be made to ensure that any information released is of the kind a client understands they have given consent for.

5b   Without the client's explicit consent

Information should be transferred beyond the agency without the client's explicit consent only in the following circumstances:

(i)   when disclosure is required by a warrant or a court order; and/or

(ii)   when non-disclosure would pose a serious risk to:
- the welfare of a child
- the safety of an employee, a volunteer, another client, or some other person; and/or

(iii) where the client is not in a position to give consent. If neither (i) nor (ii) above apply, then information may be released on an estimation of the client's best interests alone.

(See clauses 6 and 7.)

6   **Releasing information without consent**

Before information is released without consent, the issue should be raised with the client, *unless*:

(i)   this is prevented by the execution of a warrant or court order, and/or

(ii)   forewarning the client would pose risks to the safety of employees/volunteers or some other person; and/or

(iii)   circumstances prevent the client being asked for or being able to give consent.

On discussion, the client may decide to consent or to disclose the information themselves, thus avoiding problems of confidentiality for the agency.

(See clauses 7 and 8.)

7   **Authorising transfers of information without consent**

A decision to transfer information without the client's consent should be exceptional, and should be taken only following discussion with the Director of NIAS. All such transfers should be recorded and reported to the NIAS management committee.

8   **When transferring information,** *with or without the client's consent*, care should be taken to ensure that it is accurate and/or the status of the information is indicated. For example, the time period to which the information refers should be indicated, opinions should be identified as opinions, and the person holding the opinions should be identified.

All reasonable efforts should be made to check the accuracy of the information with the client or other source concerned.

9   **When transferring information,** *with or without the client's consent*:

(i)   the credentials of those who will receive the information should be verified if there is any doubt about them

(ii)   the use to which the information will be put should be discovered as far as is possible

(iii)   the employee/volunteer should assure themselves that the person to whom the information is transferred can be trusted not to misuse it

(iv)   where confidential information is transferred by post it should be clearly addressed to the person who has a right to receive it, and marked 'confidential'; and where by phone, it should be given only to the person authorised to receive it

(v)   fax and e-mail should not be used for transferring confidential information.

Information should be transferred only on a 'right-to-know' and a 'need-to-know' basis.

10   The confidentiality of third parties

When disclosing information about one client, due regard should be given to protecting the confidentiality of information about other clients.

11   Recording transfers of information

(i)   When information is transferred *with or without the client's consent*, this fact must be recorded showing, as appropriate:
–   the extent of the disclosure
–   to whom it was made and when
–   the reasons for the disclosure
–   who was consulted beforehand
–   whether the client was informed and when and how this was done.

(ii)   In the event of transfers with consent, this information will appear on the consent form.

(iii) Copies of any information transferred will also serve as a record.

12   Information for clients

All clients must be informed of this confidentiality policy, and efforts should be made to establish that they understand it. When clients are informed about the policy, they should also be informed of their rights to complain should they believe their confidentiality has been breached.

(See NIAS Complaints Procedures.)

13   In the event of a client's death

In the event of a client's death, no information will be released about him/her unless covered by clauses 5a or b and/or unless:
(i)   disclosure will correct damaging misinformation held about the client by others, and/or
(ii) non-disclosure will contribute to a miscarriage of justice.

Clause 7 applies to all such situations.

14   The client's rights of access to information

No information which is recorded about a client will be confidential from that client, and all clients have a right to see any information recorded about them unless such information compromises the confidentiality of a third party, the third party not being an employee or volunteer in the agency.

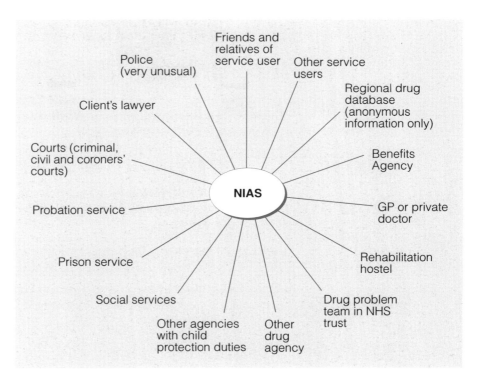

Figure 1
Other agencies and people to whom it may be necessary to transfer information about NIAS clients, with or without their consent

You can see that the policy is quite a long document. This is always the case for confidentiality policies in agencies which might have to share information about service users with other agencies. Clauses 5 to 11, 13 (and 16 and 20) all relate to transfers. That's nearly half the policy. Figure 1 gives you a picture of the kinds of transfer which might be made, with or without the client's consent, from an agency such as NIAS.

Section 2
Interpreting the policy

The activities which follow are designed to give you practice in interpreting a confidentiality policy.

2.1 Disclosure beyond the agency

The first set of activities is about confidentiality where there is a request to transfer information beyond the agency. They relate to the series of case studies below.

Jonti
Jonti is a 25-year-old drug user who is being prescribed methadone by the drug problem team of the NHS trust. NIAS is working with Jonti to help him sort out various aspects of his life, such as accommodation and personal relationships. Thus he is a client of both the drug problem team and of NIAS. Jonti has signed a consent form agreeing to NIAS discussing his affairs at drug problem team meetings where a consultant psychiatrist, community addiction nurses, a clinical psychologist and a hospital social worker will be present, as well as NIAS staff. You have reason to believe that Jonti is taking heroin in addition to his methadone. When you confront Jonti with this, he admits it but asks you not to tell the consultant, since this information may lead to his methadone prescription being withdrawn.

A worried mother
The agency is telephoned by the mother of a 13-year-old who has come to NIAS on two occasions. She demands to know what drugs her son is taking and other details of his contacts with the agency. The 13-year-old had explicitly asked that matters be kept secret from his parents.

Darren
Darren is a long-term client of the agency. He has recently been charged and found guilty of burglary, and a probation officer is preparing a pre-sentence report to help the court give an appropriate sentence. The probation officer rings NIAS and asks you to confirm that Darren is a client of the agency, because this might be an indication for a probation order rather than a custodial sentence. Currently, Darren has given no permission for his affairs to be discussed with a probation officer.

Michelle

Michelle is a heroin user and a client of NIAS. She has a child of 18 months. A social worker from the child protection team telephones NIAS to ask whether they can supply any information relevant to a case conference which will be held next week to consider whether to take Michelle's child into care. Michelle has not given any consent to her affairs being discussed with social services.

Wayne

Wayne is a client of NIAS and the drug problem team. He is a heavy user of amphetamine sulphate ('speed') which causes him to behave in ways that other people find bizarre. You are telephoned by an approved social worker (ASW), who tells you the following. (See Section 3.4 of Unit 20 for an explanation of the term 'approved social worker'.) Wayne's mother can no longer tolerate his behaviour and has asked for him to be detained in hospital under the Mental Health Act 1983 (England and Wales). Wayne has barricaded himself in the house and the police have been called to use their powers under the Mental Health Act (Section 136) to remove him to 'a place of safety'. In such circumstances an ASW is usually asked to attend. The ASW wants to know if Wayne is a drug user. People can be detained under the Mental Health Act only if they are suffering from a mental disorder. Being 'high' on amphetamine sulphate is not a mental disorder for the purpose of the Act. You are in a position to supply information which might prevent Wayne from being forcibly incarcerated in an acute psychiatric ward. Wayne has not given any consent for his affairs to be discussed with social services.

| Activity 2 | Interpreting the policy on disclosure |

Allow about 25 minutes   For each case study decide and note down what you think the NIAS confidentiality policy says that staff or volunteers should do. If you were a member of staff or a volunteer, you could always invoke the spirit of clause 7 and ask the director to make the decision. But for this activity put yourself in the director's position and decide what she ought to recommend.

Do the activity in two stages. First read each case and note down which clauses of the confidentiality policy are most relevant to it. Then, using the relevant clauses, decide what should be done.

Comment   The first case, that of **Jonti**, differs from the others since he has given permission for information about his drug-taking behaviour to be disclosed – in this case to the drug problem team. To work with him in partnership with the drug problem team you needed his permission to share information about him with them. Now he wants to go back on that undertaking. He is explicitly instructing you not to disclose this new information, so clause 5(a) no longer applies. Clause 5(b) lists the conditions under which you can disclose information without the client's consent. None of these apply to Jonti, so the policy forces you to do what he asks. However, doing this means that, as far as Jonti is concerned, you can no longer work in partnership with the drug problem team. To continue as before, behaving at drug problem team meetings as if you did not know that Jonti was taking heroin in addition to his methadone prescription, would be acting under false pretences. Of course, suddenly refusing to share information about Jonti with the team will almost certainly cause them to guess what is going on. Did anyone warn Jonti that once he had given consent, withdrawing it was likely to have this effect?

The other cases all involve telephone contacts, so you should have considered the authenticity of the callers. Clause 9(i) states, 'the credentials of those who will receive the information should be verified if there is any doubt about them. How do you know whether the caller is really the person they say they are?

None of these clients has given consent, so clause 5(b) of the policy applies. There are three sub-clauses of clause 5(b) which might provide a justification for releasing information without the client's consent.

> *Information should be transferred ... only in the following circumstances:*
>
> (i) *when disclosure is required by a warrant or a court order; and/or*
> (ii) *when non-disclosure would pose a serious risk to:*
>   – *the welfare of a child*
>   – *the safety of an employee, a volunteer, another client, or some other person; and/or*
> (iii) *where the client is not in a position to give consent. If neither (i) nor (ii) above apply, then information may be released on an estimation of the client's best interests alone.*

With regard to the **13-year-old**, 'the welfare of a child' is at risk. But there is no indication that the welfare of the child would be enhanced by disclosing the information. Under British law – in health and social care at least – so long as they understand what they are doing children have the same rights as adults to give and withhold consent, even with regard to keeping information confidential from their parents. This was established by the case of *Gillick* v. *West Norfolk and Wisbech Health Authority* in 1986. At least, that seemed to be the law in 1998. But the case mentioned concerned only doctors; another legal case concerning another kind of practitioner might decide differently. A key issue is how agencies should decide whether a child has sufficient understanding to make decisions for him- or herself, and about what. Whatever the law is, for NIAS it would be good practice to discuss with the child the possibility of a three-way meeting between parent, child and NIAS worker.

For **Darren** and **Michelle** there is an opportunity for NIAS to ask them whether they would like information to be released about them and if so what information (see clause 6). Indeed it is common practice for drug agencies to contribute to pre-sentence reports and to reports to child protection case conferences, and information is not necessarily restricted to what the client has agreed to – you will look at that in the next activity.

By contrast the case of **Wayne** is pressing and immediate. There is no time to ask for his consent, so the relevant clause of the policy is 5b(iii). Barricaded in his room, in imminent danger of being carted off, Wayne is in no position to give consent. So the question is whether it is in Wayne's best interests to release or withhold the information, always assuming that the credentials of the ASW can be verified. That's a matter for professional judgement, but the situation suggests disclosure under clause 5b(iii). The ASW will still have to decide whether (1) Wayne's behaviour is caused by the recent ingestion or injection of amphetamine sulphate or another drug – and that his behaviour is not a mental disorder, or (2) his behaviour is due to the long-term damage of taking drugs – drug-induced psychosis – which is a mental disorder for the purpose of the Mental Health Act. As an NIAS worker you will be thankful you don't have to make such decisions.

If you disclose this information about Wayne you will also have to record it (clause 11) and report this disclosure without consent to the NIAS management committee (clause 7) (although without identifying Wayne to them, as you will see when you come to read clause 17).

However, Wayne is also a client of the drug problem team. If the ASW telephoned them, and established her credentials, they would give her the information with far less hesitation than would NIAS. To understand this you might like to look back at the box in Unit 19 which outlines the doctrine of implicit consent (Section 3.2).

The comment above didn't deal fully with Darren and Michelle. You will consider them further in the next activity, but first read the following background information.

You have refused to give information about Darren or Michelle over the phone, but you arrange a visit to Darren in prison where he is on remand, and you call round to see Michelle at home.

More about Darren

Darren believes that a report from you to the probation officer (or for his lawyer to read out in court, or for you to give personally to the court) will help him avoid a custodial sentence, and you believe that in Darren's case a custodial sentence is unlikely to reform or rehabilitate him. He wants you to make a report which says that he has genuinely been trying to give up drugs, that he has been a regular attender at NIAS and has begun to respond to counselling constructively, and that he is ready and willing to go to a residential rehabilitation centre and would benefit from this. You know, however, that Darren has come to NIAS to return dirty needles and collect clean ones, and to chat with his mates in the drop-in, and hasn't really shown any serious intentions of giving up drugs.

More about Michelle

You've been worried about Michelle's infant for some time, although until now your concerns have largely arisen from things she's let slip or things said by other clients – mainly about Michelle leaving her infant to the care of other drug users for long periods of time. The actions of the child protection team have brought matters to a head. Your visit to Michelle increases your concerns. The flat is dirty and there are dirty needles in places where the child might get at them. Michelle wants you to speak on her behalf at the case conference which will decide whether her child should be taken into care or not, saying how well she looks after her child.

Activity 3   Disclosure against the service user's wishes

Allow about 25 minutes   What does the confidentiality policy suggest you should do in the cases of Darren and Michelle?

(a)   Look first at clause 8 of the policy and decide how that might apply in these two cases.

(b)   In each case you have four options:

(1)   give only information that is agreed with the client

(2)   give some information agreed with the client, and some without the client's consent

(3)   give information even though the client has not consented to any information being given

(4)   give no information at all.

Which do you think is the appropriate option in each of these two cases?

Comment   (a)   Clause 8 of the policy says:

care should be taken to ensure that [information] is accurate and/or the status of the information is indicated.

There are two ways of following this instruction. A very strict reading would mean restricting yourself to transferring information which you were absolutely certain was true. From police and courtroom dramas you may have noticed pathologists and forensic experts taking this line, or at least trying to take it in the face of pressure from lawyers for them to go beyond the evidence and to express opinions. A less strict reading would allow you to express opinions, but always indicating that they were opinions. It is worth noting, however, that even when people clearly state that something is just their opinion, this can be as influential as what they describe as a 'fact'.

Applied to the two cases, clause 8 raises the question of what NIAS really knows for sure about Darren or Michelle. For example, the NIAS worker knows for sure that there were dirty needles in reach of a toddler on the occasion of the visit, but only by hearsay that Michelle farms her infant out around her drug-using friends.

(b)   Agencies, including drug agencies, differ in the degree to which they consider themselves as advocates for those who use their services. Those most firmly committed to advocacy might take the line that they will disclose only information that is to the advantage of their client – provided that withholding other information does no serious harm to anyone else. In the case of Darren that might mean simply reporting that he regularly attended NIAS, returned his dirty needles in a responsible way, and no more. That's not quite option (1), because Darren wanted you to say a great deal more on his behalf.

No reputable agency will tell lies on behalf of its clients and in effect Darren wanted NIAS to tell lies. There is only a fine line between telling merely half the truth and telling lies. And remember that here you are being asked to make a report to a court, directly or indirectly, so the law of perjury applies. In addition, a very brief report may give rise to a suspicion that something discreditable to the service user is being withheld. On this basis, you might have decided to persuade Darren that NIAS should make no contribution to the pre-sentence report. That's option (4).

Taking options (2) or (3) might mean telling 'the truth, the whole truth and nothing but the truth'. Darren might agree to some of this being disclosed, but not all (2), or he might not give consent to your disclosing any information at all (3). You might consider disclosing information nonetheless. But you probably looked at clause 5b, and saw that in Darren's case there were no circumstances justifying disclosing information without his consent. So the policy simply doesn't allow you to take options (2) or (3).

The main difference between the case of Darren and that of Michelle centres on the welfare of her child. Clause 5b(ii) does allow you to take options (2) or (3):

Information should be transferred beyond the agency without the client's explicit consent only in the following circumstances:

[...]

(ii) when non-disclosure would pose a serious risk to:
*   –   the welfare of a child*

But again whether you would do so would depend on whether the philosophy of NIAS was primarily to advocate on behalf of its clients, or whether it saw its duty of care more broadly to give an equal priority to the welfare of clients' children. You might choose option (4) (say nothing) on the grounds that the welfare of the child was already being dealt with by other agencies, and that you had nothing to contribute which they couldn't find out themselves. Or you might choose options (2) or (3) (disclosing some information without consent), on the grounds that NIAS has a definite duty of care towards the children of service users. In Michelle's case the child protection team were already involved. But sometimes agencies such as NIAS are the first to suspect that the welfare of a child may be at risk. Then they have to make a decision whether to convey their worries to agencies which deal with child protection. You can consider this kind of decision in Activity 4.

Activity 4   **Should we alert the child protection team?**

Allow about 20 minutes   Suppose that the circumstances under which Michelle's child is being brought up are unknown to social services, or health visitors, or any other workers in the statutory services. Only NIAS has seen that there is some cause for concern. What steps does the policy suggest should be taken in this case and what other actions do you think would be appropriate?

Note: Some drug agencies receiving some of their funding from social services have a contractual obligation to report children who might be 'at risk'. That means they risk losing their funding if they don't. For this activity assume that NIAS has no such contractual obligation.

Comment   This question goes a little beyond confidentiality practice, but it is fairly easy to take the spirit of the policy and see what other actions it suggests the agency might take.

You may have proposed something like this. If NIAS is concerned about the welfare of Michelle's child, it should raise the issue with her and try to work with her to provide a safer environment for the child. The safe management of needles and drugs in the home is standard work for a drugs agency, and it won't do Michelle any good if her child is injured, infected, neglected or poisoned with drugs. At the same time, however, the confidentiality policy implies (clause 5b(ii)) that NIAS will alert child protection if it feels that Michelle's behaviour *continues* to put her child at risk. This is something which should be conveyed to Michelle (clause 6), and should be acted on if circumstances warrant it. It may be that Michelle can be persuaded herself to approach social services or health visitors for assistance in childcare. However, recommending that she does depends on a careful estimation of what they are likely to do, and whether it will be to the advantage of Michelle and/or the child.

Since you have now done a lot of thinking about Michelle and her child it is worth exploring the implications of the policy if the worst happened in this case.

Activity 5 | **Legal requirements to disclose**

Allow about 10 minutes | The statutory authorities have not been involved. NIAS has been working with Michelle to try to minimise the risks to her child. But the child eats some tranquilliser tablets. According to Michelle, these were left lying around unbeknown to her by a visitor to her flat. The child dies. An inquest is convened. You are called to give evidence. What does the policy say about disclosing information in court?

Comment | Actually, it doesn't matter what the policy says. If the court requires you to give evidence then you have a choice between giving evidence or being punished for contempt of court, and between answering the questions asked of you honestly, or risking being found guilty of perjury. Half-truths can count as perjury or as 'obstructing the course of justice'.

If the policy asked you to do otherwise it could not be binding and you could not be dismissed from your job for giving evidence in court despite clause 1. Nor would it be any defence in court to say that you were bound by the agency policy not to disclose any information. However, the policy does actually accord with the law (clause 5b(i)) while clause 8 suggests that in court you should try to stick to the facts and as far as possible avoid being drawn into expressing unsubstantiated opinions.

The activities above are not suitable for inclusion in a portfolio. So much comment was provided that it would be unclear whether your response was your own work or not. The next activity, however, is not followed by comment, so it would be suitable as an entry in a portfolio. Section 4.2 gives you advice on how to prepare items for inclusion in a portfolio.

Confidentiality policies sometimes do not give a clear answer as to what actions should be taken. And sometimes they may appear to indicate actions which seem unwise under the particular circumstances. In such situations the question to ask is: 'Would more harm come from keeping matters confidential than from disclosing them?' Activity 6 invites you to ask this question about the scenario below.

A stabbing on Christmas Eve

On Christmas Eve Marion, the director of NIAS, was talking to a client in the agency. Another client came in and an altercation started between the two. The first client stabbed the newcomer and then ran away. Marion administered first aid to a flesh wound in the upper arm and then took the injured client to A&E. The client who carried out the stabbing was on parole and, if his probation officer were told of the event, this would probably result in his being returned

> to prison and being charged with an additional offence. The altercation was about some illegal business and the client who was stabbed was insistent that the matter should not be reported to the police.
>
> NIAS has no contractual obligation to the probation service to report to them on the behaviour of its clients.

Activity 6

Allow about 30 minutes

Trouble on Christmas Eve

(a)   Look at the NIAS confidentiality policy (clause 5b in particular), and list the options it allows Marion to take.

(b)   Fill in the grid below.

	Harm which might be done by keeping the information confidential	**Harm which might be done by disclosing the information**
To the agency	*Maybe held accountable*	*Reputation – full responsibility*
To the worker	*✓*	*Maybe held accountable*
To the client who did the stabbing	*May need to be specialist psychiatric help.*	*Will be charged with offence – imprisoned*
To the client who was stabbed	*Incident may re-occur.*	*Investigation of illegal business*
To the probation service	*Should be considered of further offence.*	*Negligence issues?*
To the public	*May endanger other members of public*	*Loss of confidence in NIAS service*

(c)   Decide what Marion should have done. The policy itself does not provide a right answer.

(d)   This incident will have to be recorded in an incident book, and reported to the management committee of NIAS. Write a report to the management committee describing what happened, indicating your decision, and justifying it. In order to justify the decision you will need to indicate the options available (question (a) above) and say why you adopted the option(s) you chose and rejected the others. Before you write your report have a look forward to clause 17 of the confidentiality policy in Section 2.2.

It might be a good idea to try your justification out on a friend or colleague, allowing them to read the confidentiality policy.

Section 5.3 in this unit deals with report writing. If you are going to include the report in a portfolio, make sure you read Section 5.3 and do Activity 18 before you write the final version.

2.2 Managing gossip

The remainder of the NIAS confidentiality policy is given below. It is mainly about managing information within the agency.

Confidentiality policy: NIAS (clauses 15–20)

The management of information in the agency

15   Identification of clients in recorded information

     (i)   Recorded information which identifies clients will be secured in the lockable filing cabinets.

     (ii)   No information which identifies clients by name will be recorded on the computer.

     (iii)   Information which identifies clients will not be left unsecured, lying around in the agency.

16   Transfer of recorded information

No recorded information which identifies clients should ever leave the premises of NIAS *unless*:

     (i)   it is being transferred according to the conditions in clauses 5a or 5b and under the terms of clauses 6, 8 and 9 as appropriately applied, and/or

     (ii)   the front sheet identifying the client is removed from the file whenever case files need to be taken to a client's home, a case conference or some other necessary place.

17   Discussion of clients within NIAS

     (i)   Discussions among employees/volunteers concerning clients should be purposeful and should not take the form of gossip.

     (ii)   Only rarely will the management committee have need to know the name of a particular client. For discussions at management committee meetings the anonymity of clients should be maintained unless the discussion concerns:

         •   a formal complaint by the client (see NIAS Complaints Procedure)

         •   the exclusion of the client from the agency (see NIAS policy on conditions for clients using the agency)

         •   a matter where the identify of the client and the relevant issue have entered the public domain.

     Even in the circumstances noted above the management committee should consider whether affairs can be dealt with without identifying the client.

18   Discussion of clients with others

     (i)   The affairs of a client should never be discussed in the hearing of other clients, unless this is satisfactory to the client concerned, nor in the hearing of any visitor who does not have a right to receive such information.

     (ii)   Should members of the agency notice each other, or clients, disclosing confidential information about others in this way, they should draw attention to what is happening.

19   Extent of recorded information

To reduce the possibilities for breaches of confidentiality, information which is recorded *and is attributable to an individual* should be:

(i)   the minimum consistent with the work of the agency, and

(ii) in the employee's/volunteer's opinion not of a kind which might cause harm or embarrassment to the client concerned, or to another client *unless* required by the agency, and

(iii) be agreed with the client, *except for:*

- matters concerning behaviour on the premises which breaches the conditions for clients using the agency (see NIAS policy on conditions for clients using the agency), and/or

- matters which if not recorded might pose a threat to health or safety (see clause 5b (ii)).

20   Retention of records

Records attributable to individuals will be retained for a period of three years after the last contact with the client. After this they will be destroyed. Only on very rare occasions will information be disclosed from the records of a client who has ceased to have contact with the agency. Clause 7 applies. (See also clause 13.)

As noted in Unit 19, gossip usually constitutes a greater risk to confidentiality than does unauthorised disclosure from recorded information. Clause 18 of the NIAS policy is an attempt to deal with this. Just writing things down in a policy document is rarely enough to ensure that people abide by the policy, so the next activity considers the need for training. You might use your response to this activity as an item in a portfolio.

Activity 7   **Training against gossip**

Allow about 30 minutes: longer if you are going to include the response in a portfolio

Imagine that you are going to run a training course for NIAS volunteers and that the danger of gossip is going to feature in it. For the training course write three brief scenarios illustrating:

(a)   the dangers of a volunteer discussing an NIAS client with a spouse or partner or friend of the volunteer

(b)   a volunteer under pressure from one service user to discuss the affairs of another

(c)   a situation in which service users might overhear another service user giving confidential information about him/herself to a volunteer.

You are going to use the scenarios in the training course to get the volunteers to tell you:

(1)   what dangers might arise from each situation

(2)   what action they should have taken or should take to prevent this happening.

Your response to the activity should be the scenarios, and for each a list of the points you want the volunteers to have learnt from them.

There is no comment for this activity, but see Section 4.2 for advice on how you might use it in a portfolio.

Section 3
The policy for service users and researchers

3.1 Informing service users

The confidentiality policy you have been working on was written for people who work in the agency, whether as paid workers or volunteers. Although there is no reason why the agency's clients should not read it, it is not a particularly 'client-friendly' document. The policy itself requires clients to be told what the policy is (clause 12) and this implies being told in a way that they will understand without too much trouble. The principles are the same as those discussed in Unit 18 about communicating with service users in ways they find useful.

Activity 8

Allow about 25 minutes: longer if you are going to include the response in a portfolio

The policy for clients

For this activity write a statement on confidentiality suitable for clients which:

- is brief, but contains as much information as most clients need most of the time
- is suitable for display as a poster (i.e. in large lettering) on the wall of the agency
- is written in a language clients will understand, without distorting the content of the policy
- addresses what you think will be their major concerns
- tells them that they can read the full policy if they like, or ask a member of staff to explain the policy more fully
- informs them of their right to complain if they think their confidentiality has been breached.

There will be no comment to this activity, so that if you include it in a portfolio you can say that it is all your own work. But check whether your response successfully accomplishes the task set. You could do this by getting someone else to read your statement and asking them whether they think it would answer the kinds of questions a service user might ask.

3.2 Confidentiality and research

When NIAS drew up its confidentiality policy no one thought about the possibility of information about NIAS clients featuring in research. So when a researcher approached NIAS with a request to do research on their clients the management committee had to consider how the spirit of their confidentiality policy might be made to apply to this new situation.

Activity 9   Confidentiality and research

Allow about 30 minutes   The researcher wants to research only into the experiences of women who began taking drugs before the age of 25. Such women are only some of NIAS's diverse clientele. The researcher wants to interview them and compare what they tell her with what appears on the 'case files' held by NIAS.

Read through NIAS's confidentiality policy again. Work out procedures which might be adopted in order for NIAS to co-operate with the researcher, without breaching the letter or the spirit of its own confidentiality policy. Consider both:

(1)   keeping information confidential from the researcher, should the clients wish this

(2)   keeping confidential any information the researcher does obtain about clients.

Write up the result of this activity as a report with recommendations to the NIAS management committee. You might begin something like this:

> *We have been approached by a researcher who wishes to conduct research into the experience of drug using by women who began taking drugs before they reached the age of 25, using the experience of our clients as part of the research. The nature of the research requires the researcher to identify which of our clients fall into the relevant group, to interview these, and to read the NIAS case notes about them. I was asked to draw up some procedures which we and the researcher might follow so that we could co-operate without breaching the spirit of our confidentiality policy. These are my recommendations ...*

There is no comment for this activity, but see Section 4.2 for advice on how you might present your answer in a portfolio. Section 5.3 in this unit deals with report writing, so if you are going to include this report in a portfolio make sure that you read Section 5.3 and do Activity 18 before you produce the final version.

Section 4

Consolidating your practice learning

The activities in Sections 2 and 3 gave you some opportunities to work with a particular confidentiality policy. However, this also involved you in other types of work which are fairly common practices in health and social care: see Table 1.

Table 1   Other types of work

	Activity number							
What you did	**2**	**3**	**4**	**5**	**6**	**7**	**8**	**9**
Read and interpreted a policy or code of practice	✔	✔	✔	✔	✔	✔	✔	✔
Explained a policy or code of practice to others						✔	✔	
Made a considered and justifiable judgement where a policy or code of practice gave no definitive guidance					✔			✔
Wrote a report for a particular readership					✔			✔
Prepared some training materials and thought about their use						✔		
Wrote some information materials for service users							✔	

4.1 Reviewing your learning

The activity below asks you to review what you have learnt and to consider how it might be transferred to other health or social care practices.

Activity 10   **Reviewing transferable learning**

Allow about 15 minutes   For this activity fill in the grid opposite or draw your own, bigger, version if necessary. In the first column jot down what you think you learnt about confidentiality practice from this unit. In the second column jot down how you think the learning could be transferred. For example, interpreting confidentiality policies is very similar to interpreting other policies or codes of practice. In the last column try to identify any further knowledge or any further opportunities for practice you need to gain. If you are aiming for a VQ then you should do this last part of the activity with the advice of your mentor and with the standards for your VQ scheme beside you.

What you did	What did you learn about confidentiality practice in particular?	To what other practices could the learning be transferred?	What more do you need to know/ practise?
Interpreted a policy document			
Explained a policy to others			
Made a justifiable judgement where the policy gave no definitive guidance			
Wrote a report			
Prepared training materials			
Wrote information for service users			

4.2 Adding to your K100 portfolio

The activities shown in Table 2 are suitable for inclusion in a K100 portfolio. They are probably suitable for a VQ portfolio too, but to establish this you will need to read the VQ assessment scheme relevant to you, as advised in the K100 Pathways VQ Guide.

Table 2   Portfolio activities

Activity number	End product	Demonstrates competence in:
6	Report to management committee	• Interpreting written policy • Making a judgement where policy provides no definitive guidance • Writing a report for a particular readership
7	Set of three scenarios and teaching notes detailing feedback to volunteers and showing what you hoped they would have learnt	• Interpreting written policy • Explaining a written policy to others • Preparing training materials • Preparing a scheme of work for using training materials
8	Text suitable for display as a poster	• Interpreting written policy • Explaining a written policy to others • Writing materials suitable for service users
9	Set of recommendations (report) to management committee	• Interpreting written policy • Making a judgement where policy provides no definitive guidance • Writing a report for a particular readership

Anyone reading your portfolio will need to know what the items in it represent. None of these items makes much sense without the NIAS confidentiality policy, so you will need to photocopy that to include in your portfolio. None of the items will make much sense without an explanation of the task that generated them. For this you could simply make copies of the activity instructions, or you could find another way of explaining what these items resulted from. And none of them makes much sense in *portfolio terms* unless you say what skills or competences each item is evidence of. One way of expressing this is in the last column of Table 2. But be careful if you are designing a portfolio for a particular assessment scheme. Each scheme will have its own vocabulary for describing skills or competences, and you will need to use the terms current in that scheme.

Section 5
Study skills

5.1 Reading scatter diagrams

So far in K100 you have looked at numbers presented in the form of
tables, bar charts and pie charts. Now you will see another way of
presenting them – as a scatter diagram (sometimes scattergram for
short). You can see an example in Figure 2 overleaf. The particular
numbers you will focus on are to do with the allocation of resources for
mental health care to different districts of London. As you might expect,
districts vary in the need for mental health care.

> *The need for mental health care varies widely with local characteristics,
> particularly with social deprivation, leading to a four or fivefold difference
> in the need for resources in different areas ... Hospital admission rates for
> different populations – a good 'proxy' for need – vary by a factor of five
> and are associated with social factors such as the number of people living
> alone and in poverty. A reasonably accurate way of predicting admission
> rates is based on Brian Jarman's underprivileged area scores – the so-
> called Jarman 8, which combines eight of these social factors.*
>
> *(Audit Commission, 1994, p. 10)*

Activity 11   Hospital admission rates and the Jarman 8 index

Allow about 10 minutes   (a)   What do you think is meant by hospital admission rates being a good
proxy for need? Why would you want a proxy?

(b)   What does the Jarman 8 index measure?

Comment   (a)   The need for health care in different localities is a complicated (and
therefore expensive) thing to measure, whereas when people are
admitted to hospital their home address and the nature of their need
are routinely recorded. So hospital admissions records offer data
which can be analysed to see, for each local district, how many
people are admitted for mental health care. These admission rates
can then be used as a 'proxy' for fully researched estimates of local
need. (This is similar to a proxy vote, where someone votes on behalf
of someone else.) But admission rates certainly are not a perfect
measure of local need. For example, some people who need mental
health care do not seek it, possibly because they are not aware of
their need; others pay for private treatment. However, the authors of
the Audit Commission report tell us that hospital admission rates are a
'good' proxy for need (on the basis of previous research comparing
admission rates with other measures of need for treatment).

(b)   The Jarman index is a measure of how socially deprived an area is.
It is obtained by combining figures for eight social factors (such as
numbers of people living alone and in poverty). According to the
Audit Commission report, the Jarman score for an area is a good
predictor of admission rates to hospitals: if you know the Jarman
score for an area, you can make a good guess at how many people
will be admitted to hospital for mental health problems. So the
Jarman score is also a good indicator of the level of need for mental
health care.

The Audit Commission was interested in whether the level of *need* for mental health care in different London districts bears any relationship to how much is *spent* on mental health care in those districts. They took as their measure of need the Jarman score for each district.

Study skills: Figures which stand for figures

So the Jarman score is used because it is a good predictor of hospital admissions rates, which are a good proxy for mental health care needs. It is a figure standing for a figure which stands for another figure. Social scientists have to be flexible and cunning in making use of the data available. Time and cost impose severe constraints. You are seldom in a position to get exactly the figures you want, but you may be able to get a pretty good estimate by working from other figures.

Look now at Figure 2. You can see why diagrams like this are called scatter diagrams. It is because they show how some things are scattered or distributed. The dots which are scattered on the diagram are health districts. If this were a map, you would read it to see how health districts were scattered in space: north, south, east and west of each other. But in this case the diagram shows how the districts are distributed, on the one hand in terms of how much they spend on mental health services, and on the other in terms of the local need for mental health services. This is still a kind of mapping, but not in terms of spatial positions.

*   First look at the horizontal line (called the 'horizontal axis'). It shows Jarman scores ranging from −40 (low need) at the left to 80 (high need) at the right.

*   Then look at the vertical line (or vertical axis). It shows expenditure on mental health, ranging from £180 per head (per annum) to £0.

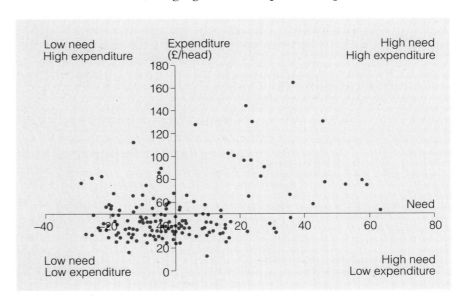

Figure 2
The relationship between need for mental health care and expenditure in London districts (Audit Commission, 1994, p. 12, 'Exhibit 6')

Activity 12   **Interpreting a scatter diagram 1**

Allow about 5 minutes   (a)   How high, roughly, is the highest expenditure per head on mental health care?

(b)   How low, roughly, is the lowest expenditure?

(c)   What, roughly, is the highest Jarman score of any district?

(d)   What, roughly, is the lowest Jarman score of any district?

(e)   Can you see what the average expenditure per head is?

Comment   (a)   About £165 per head per annum. You need to find the highest dot on the diagram (up and towards the right). This dot stands for the district with the highest expenditure. If you look left from the dot to the vertical axis you will see it is just slightly above 160 but not as far as half-way to 180. You can't do better than a rough guess of about 165.

(b)   About £10–15 per head. The lowest dot is just to the right of the vertical axis. You can see that the dot is below 20, but not as far as half-way down to 0.

(c)   About 63–64 is my estimate. You are looking for the dot furthest over to the right. It is just above the horizontal axis. Remember this high score means the district is very needy.

(d)   Getting towards –30. That is the dot furthest over to the left – standing for the district with the least need.

(e)   Nearly £50 per head. The horizontal axis cuts across the vertical axis between 40 and 60 – say 48. (The average Jarman score is 0.) Not all scatter diagrams allow you to read off an average in this way – it depends how the axes are drawn.

Don't worry if you found question (e) difficult to answer.

You now have the general gist of what this diagram is about. It shows districts of London, represented as dots, and the position of each dot shows how much was spent per head in that district and how needy it is.

Activity 13   **Interpreting a scatter diagram 2**

Allow about 5 minutes   (a)   Are there districts which have high need and which also spend a lot on mental health care?

(b)   Are there districts which have high need but don't spend much on mental health care?

(c)   Do the districts with the lowest need spend least on mental health care?

(d)   Is there a relationship between the level of need in districts and the amount they spend on mental health care?

Comment   (a)   The seven dots which are furthest over to the right (highest need) are all above the horizontal line (above average expenditure). Also the five highest dots (highest spending) are to the right of the vertical line (above average need). In fact all the districts which fall in the top-right part of the diagram are above average for both need and spending. So the answer is – yes, there are a lot of districts with high need which spend a lot.

(b)   There are many dots which fall to the right of the vertical line (some with need scores nearly as high as 40) and also below the horizontal line (below average expenditure). So the answer is – yes, there are districts with high need which don't spend much.

(c)   There are some dots well to the left (low need) which are also well above the horizontal line (above average expenditure). In fact, although there are plenty of low-need districts which are below average spenders (bottom left), there are also plenty which are above average (top left). So – no, you can't say that the districts with the lowest need spend least.

(d)   If there were a very clear relationship between need and spending, the dots would tend to fall in a straight line running from bottom left to top right. In other words, the higher the need score, the higher the spending score; and the lower the need score, the lower the spending score. But these dots are scattered all over the place. They don't look at all like a straight line. So there is certainly not a strong relationship between the two. However, the fact that there are no dots in the far top left, or the far bottom right, indicates a slight relationship.

When a scatter diagram like this shows the dots all tending to fall close to a line from bottom left to top right, then it shows a strong *correlation*. A correlation means that two things vary together. For example, taller people tend to be heavier. So height and weight are correlated; but not perfectly, because some short people are heavy and some tall people are light. Correlations are often expressed as a number – a correlation coefficient. A perfect positive correlation is expressed as 1.0. It hardly ever happens in reality. Negative correlations are also possible. For example, the vertical position of the two ends of a see-saw shows a perfect negative correlation (–1.0) because however high up one end is, the other end must be a corresponding distance down. Perfect negative correlations hardly ever happen either. Coefficients greater than 0.8 or less than –0.8 are taken to indicate very strong correlations. Zero indicates no correlation at all. On the diagram you have been looking at there is a very weak positive correlation between expenditure and need, probably around 0.1. You can't see it by looking at the diagram.

There are many ways in which correlations can be calculated and expressed. Scatter diagrams are only one of them.

> **Study skills: Scatter diagrams and correlations**
>
> You will not need to go any further with scatter diagrams and correlations in K100. You don't need to know how to create a scatter diagram, although you can probably work out for yourself how this is done. And for this course you certainly don't need to be able to do the statistics necessary to calculate a correlation. But it is useful to know how to read scatter diagrams, because they crop up in books and articles about health and social care.
>
> Up to a point you can see whether there is any strong correlation shown on a scatter diagram. If there is one, most of the dots will fall close to a diagonal line, running bottom left to top right for a positive correlation, or top left to bottom right for a negative one. There may be a weaker correlation even if you can't see one clearly on the diagram. But to find that out you would have to do some rather complicated statistics. Sometimes scatter diagrams are published with a correlation coefficient – somewhere between 1.0

and –1.0. All you need to know about this is that the nearer the number is to zero, the weaker the correlation is, whether the figure is plus or minus.

So what have you found out by working on this diagram? Basically, it shows that although the need for mental health care is a great deal higher in some districts of London than others, and although spending per head is 10 times as high in some districts as in others, there is very little relationship between need and spending. Some districts (top left) with relatively low need are spending quite a lot, but more worryingly, some (bottom right) with high need are spending relatively little. As far as your number skills are concerned you have:

- learnt how to read a scatter diagram
- been introduced to the idea of a correlation.

5.2 More thoughts about the exam

Now we return to the theme running through all the later skills units – preparing for the K100 exam.

Voices of experience

To begin you will listen to four people who have already taken Open University exams. You will hear what their feelings are about exams and how they try to get the best out of themselves at exam time.

Activity 14   **Coping with exams**

Allow about 20 minutes

First read the Media Notes so that you know who you will be listening to. Then write these headings down the side of a sheet of paper:

1   Feelings about exams
2   Ways of coping with anxiety
3   When to start revision
4   Strategies for revision
5   Tips.

You can make notes under these headings as you listen.

Then listen to side 2 of Audio Cassette 5.

When you have finished, note down any more points you think might be useful to remember. Then, under each of the five headings, summarise your conclusions from the discussion.

Comment   Here are some of the ideas you may have jotted down.

1   It helps to look the exam ogre straight in the eye. Then you know that this is what you are up against – this is as bad as it gets. So on the cassette each person was asked to think of their worst exam experiences. For all of them exams tend to be something of an ordeal. But all felt they had learnt to come to terms with the pressures by taking control of the revision process.

2   Like most people, these students felt pretty wound up over the final weeks and days and especially on exam day. However, they found they were able to settle down once the exam started. Some

mentioned taking deep breaths at the start and reading the paper very carefully to get themselves focused. In her first exam Gwyneth got into a flap, knocking over her drink, but her second exam she said she quite 'enjoyed'.

3   These students all started their revision at least a month before the exam. Three started in August. (It's worth pointing out, though, that all three were studying 30-point courses, whereas K100 is twice that size and continues three weeks into September.) Perhaps Jenny's experience of starting her D103 revision in September is a more realistic guide. You should be starting K100 Unit 28 mid-way through September (a short unit designed to help with your revision). That seems a reasonable target date to be swinging into a full-scale attack on revision. You might begin some preliminary sorting out and dipping back into things before then, but don't let worries about the exam spoil the last part of the course for you. With all the key points boxes, K100 is a fairly straightforward course to revise. You should be able to complete a pretty thorough review in two or three weeks.

4   As you heard in the discussion, revision is not just a dreary plod through the course a second time. It should be much more active and creative than that. One very strong message which comes through is the importance of organisation and planning. After the interview each of the four was asked to write down their three top tips for revision. Of the 12 tips, eight related to organisation and planning.

5   Towards the end of the discussion Julie offered some general tips: don't panic, enjoy the course, but don't leave everything to the last minute, and set about your revision in a planned, methodical way – then you'll start to feel more comfortable and confident. Here are some of the tips the others wrote down after the discussion.

   •   Go through past exam papers and look at questions. Look at course material related to the questions. Decide on your strengths and weaknesses and work on the weaknesses.

   •   Go through your notes and make new notes.

   •   Brainstorm the main titles of the course and do a 'mind map' – it will be a useful guide.

Study skills: Making yourself look ahead

Has listening to the discussion helped to put the K100 exam into perspective? Has it made the exam seem more 'real' and in a sense 'ordinary' – something that will just happen one day and then be over and part of your past, not a vague and mysterious threat looming in the distance? The clearest message that comes from what these students said is the importance of thinking ahead well before the exam – not leaving things to the last minute, when it is too late to get yourself properly organised. As Gwyneth, who got into such difficulties first time, wrote, 'Don't cram – always make sure you have enough time for everything.'

Exam anxiety

Yet however 'rational' and organised you manage to be about the exam, you are likely to experience some anxiety. As you read in Section 1 of Chapter 7 of *The Good Study Guide*, exams put you under pressure. This has both good and bad effects. Stress supplies the energy and motivation to push you to peak performances and bring out your true ability. But if stress isn't controlled and channelled it can also lead to a build-up of anxiety, to a point where it begins to have bad effects both on your exam performance and on you.

Bad effects of anxiety

It's important to look at the common effects of anxiety, so that you can recognise them and work out ways of overcoming them.

Avoidance: putting off thinking about the exam. 'Avoidance' is a common psychological response to uncomfortable situations. You find ways of absorbing your mind with other things (which normally scarcely interest you at all). Deep down you know that putting off facing up to the challenge is making the situation worse. But the worse the situation gets, the greater your incentive to avoid thinking about it. You become ever more creative at finding other 'very important' things to attend to – it's a vicious circle. Then you end up, two days before the exam, facing reality at last but in a complete panic and with no hope of doing yourself justice.

Difficulty with concentration: getting into a state of agitation such that you can't stay focused on anything. You stop frequently to worry about how little time is left and how much you still have to cover; you blame yourself for what you haven't done; you dither and switch from one thing to another, so that you never dwell for long enough to really fix anything in your mind – in short, you spend a lot of time not achieving very much.

Distorted perception and poor judgement: getting the exam out of proportion, so that it seems a life or death struggle; failing to recognise how much you have learnt during the year; feeling that you must cover every last bit of the course, instead of playing to your strengths; thinking you should memorise long lists of facts; hoping that putting most of your time into one really good answer will offset other weaker answers; thinking the exam will be designed to catch you out, instead of recognising that it is just about what you've read in the course. In other words you get blown off course by all those myths you read about in Chapter 7 of *The Good Study Guide*.

Distress: then there is the miserable feeling itself; doubting that all your investment in K100 is worth while; wishing you were a different person; losing sleep; being a gloomy burden to those around you.

Loss of function: not being able to do things that you normally do perfectly easily. (Recently, an acquaintance failed her driving test. The first thing she was asked to do was reverse round a corner and she completely forgot what to do, although she had never had trouble with the manoeuvre before.) You can read more about this in Section 5.2, 'Changes to your mental powers', in Chapter 7 of *The Good Study Guide*. Even though you don't yet need to plan your final couple of days before the exam, read Sections 5.2 to 5.5 now. They will give you a sense of why it is so helpful to start preparing early – and how you can organise your work to take advantage of the effects that anxiety is likely to have on you.

These, then, are some of the ways anxiety can undermine your work towards the exam. What is more, anxiety has a tendency to feed off itself, as Figure 3 shows.

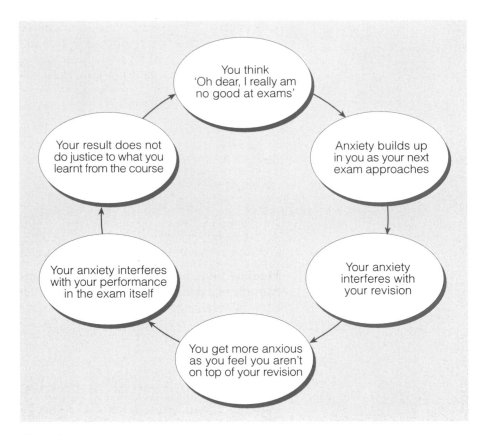

Figure 3
The vicious circle of anxiety

Obviously, you want to break out of this vicious circle if you can, or better still avoid getting into it. But how?

Keeping anxiety under control

Planning and organisation. The main way our four students tackled anxiety was by starting preparations early, before tensions had begun to build up. They then kept themselves busy with carefully organised preparations until the exam. This helps to reduce anxiety through:

- redirecting nervous energy into productive channels

- reassuring you that your prospects of success are improving hour by hour, as you revise

- giving a feeling of being in control of anxiety rather than driven by it.

Avoiding avoidance. It is important to work out ways of cutting through your own avoidance strategies. One way is to set yourself short, undemanding tasks to start with (like sorting out your course materials). Jenny said she found listening again to some of the audio cassettes a non-taxing way of 'getting into it'. Once you get yourself started on *any* exam-relevant task, you begin to break the cycle of avoidance – preventing the build-up of a deep-seated sense of not being able to cope.

Talking yourself down. Another line of attack is to keep reminding yourself what the real priorities of life are so that you maintain a sense of proportion. Of course exams are important, but they are not the most important things in life. In any case, taking them too seriously is counter-productive. You end up doing badly because you are so concerned to do well. Keep glancing back at the early parts of Chapter 7 of *The Good Study Guide*, if it helps.

Talking to other people. Probably the best way of getting exams in proportion is talking to other people, especially when you are studying in isolation most of the time. It's easy to think you are the only person who is having difficulties. Julie says she runs up a huge phone bill just before exams, talking to a friend. Other people find meeting fellow students at tutorials reassuring. Sometimes family members can help. If you have tried all these and still feel anxious, have a talk with your tutor.

Relaxation techniques. There are many ways of relaxing yourself when you are stressed: going for walks, playing sports, evenings out with friends, yoga, listening to relaxation cassettes. One very useful technique is to sit still and upright, and breathe deeply for a minute or two. You need to find out what works for you. It is worth getting a leaflet from your doctor, or browsing along the shelves of a bookshop or library, to give yourself some new ideas to try out.

Medical help. Some people find that none of these approaches is enough in itself. If you are in any doubt as to whether you can stay on top of your exam nerves, consult your doctor. Don't just suffer in isolation. After putting so many hours of work into the course, you don't want to run the risk of letting yourself down in the exam. Make sure you get the help you need.

Study skills: Beating exam anxiety

Most of us feel anxious before exams. So it is important to:
- be aware of effects that anxiety can have on you as you prepare for and take the exam
- work out ways of overcoming anxiety.

Anxiety can have a variety of effects, which people cope with in different ways. But in essence it comes down to:
- facing up to the exam
- getting clear in your mind *what* you need to do and *how* you will go about it
- talking to other people
- getting working (instead of worrying).

Don't let anxiety get you down. As you read in Unit 17, this is your course. You have paid for the exam. Get what *you* need from it. Don't let it get the upper hand. Use the tension to get the best out of yourself.

So what can you begin to do now, nearly three months away from the exam? I suggest that one thing is to take a close look at the specimen exam paper and another is to begin to sketch out a revision timetable.

Reviewing the specimen exam paper

You will receive a specimen exam paper around this time.

Activity 15   **The specimen exam paper**

Allow about 20 minutes   Read carefully through your specimen exam paper, including all the instructions.

(a) *Structure of the paper.* Notice that the exam is in three parts.

    (i) What does this mean in terms of how you spend your time in the exam?

    (ii) What does it suggest in terms of what you need to revise?

(b) Do the questions look familiar? Can you see what kind of answers are needed?

(c) Read questions 1 to 5 carefully. Underline key words. (Use pencil so that you can change your mind later.)

(d) How does looking at the questions make you feel?

Comment   (a) Structure of the exam paper

    (i) You have to answer three questions in three hours. All questions are worth the same number of marks. So you should spend roughly an hour on each of your three questions.

    (ii) You have to choose one question from each of the three parts of the paper. The questions in Part I are from Blocks 1, 2 and 3 of the course. The questions in Part II are from Blocks 4, 5 and 6. The questions in Part III are either directly from Block 7 or are about the course as a whole. **This means that you don't need to revise the whole course in detail for the exam.** You *must* revise Block 7, but you could get away with revising just one block out of the first three and one from the next three. However, that would leave you without any choice. So, just in case there is a question which does not suit you, it is safer to have a 'back-up' block for each of Parts I and II. In other words a reasonable revision strategy is to **focus your revision on Block 7, plus two blocks out of the first three, and two blocks out of the next three.**

(b) The general form of the questions ought to look pretty familiar. They are very similar to the questions asked in the TMAs. Obviously you can't write anything like such a long answer when you only have an hour. But the basic principles are the same, so you should approach your answers in the same way you approach TMAs.

(c) You haven't done your studies for questions 6 to 9 yet, but questions 1 to 5 ought to have rung a few bells for you as you did your underlining. Was it obvious to you that question 1 was on Block 1, question 2 on Block 2, and so on? Don't worry if you can't think of all that you might want to put into your answers. The main point is to reassure yourself that you can actually make sense of the questions and that you can see how the questions link to the blocks. Once you start to revise, the key ideas in the blocks will start to come back to you.

(d) Did you find the first sight of the exam paper a bit nerve-wracking? Lots of people say they do. A very common first reaction is to think you can't make any sense of the questions at all. But as you underline key words you begin to see that the questions are more or less what you would expect. As you work on the paper during your revision, and develop plans for tackling it, the general structure and format will become a lot more familiar and less daunting.

A three-part paper

The idea behind having three parts to the exam is quite straightforward. Parts I and II give you an incentive to consolidate your understanding, both of the early blocks of the course and of the later blocks. But we also wanted to give you a chance to show how your wider understanding of care has developed during the year, so Part III gives you that opportunity. At the same time Part III is the only assessment for Block 7. (There is no TMA for Block 7, to avoid putting additional pressures on you in the last stages of the course.) This works out well because Block 7 takes a broad view of care issues and aims to bring the course together. One of the Part III questions will link to Unit 26 and another to Unit 27. The third question will be a more general one on a broad issue running through the course. Unit 28 gives you help in looking at the course this way.

You can write very good answers in Parts I and II simply by focusing on the block that corresponds to the question number. If it turns out that you are also able to draw on what you have learnt in other blocks, that may make an answer even better. But let this come to you, if it happens. Don't feel you have to strive for cross-block connections. Keep your sights on doing justice to what you know of the particular block. Part III is where you have the chance to write more broadly, bringing together ideas from across the course.

What is a good exam answer?

The basic principles of the exam questions are much the same as for TMAs, although obviously answers are shorter and not as detailed as when you have your books around you. To get a clearer picture of what examiners look for in answers turn now to *The Good Study Guide* and read Section 3 of Chapter 7.

Study skills: Squaring up to the exam paper

As you see, there is no great mystery about the exam paper. You just write three answers of the kind that you have been writing all through the course, but shorter. The links between the questions and the course are quite clear and you have plenty of choice over what parts of the course to write about. Perhaps you felt a bit reluctant as you began exploring the specimen paper, but now you have had a good look you can see that it's pretty straightforward.

Drawing up a rough time plan

For now, all that remains is to begin to think about when you will start your revision. The students on the cassette were very clear about the advantages of doing this. Here are some of the 'key tips' they wrote down:

- time management – give yourself plenty of time
- decide when you are going to start revision and what time you can set aside for it
- plan revision before you start
- do a timetable of how/when/where you should be, so that you can make sure you have covered all the areas of the course.

You don't need to do a detailed plan yet, just a general sketch of the overall timescale and when you think you will get your best opportunities for revision. More detailed planning will be discussed in Unit 28.

Activity 16

Planning your revision

Allow about 15 minutes

Draw a chart showing the next 12 weeks or so up to the exam (a 12 x 7 grid, with days along one edge and weeks along the other) or use a calendar or diary. Write in holidays and any other major disruptions you anticipate. Put the units you have not read yet in the weeks you hope to study them. Fill in TMAs and tutorials and the date of the exam. Now sketch in where you think your main chunks of exam preparation time will come.

Looking at what you have marked as preparation time, and thinking about how much time you normally manage to set aside for studying per week, estimate how many hours overall you hope to be able to find for revision.

Comment

Obviously, the amount of time you can find for revision depends on your circumstances. There is no absolute requirement. You make the best use you can of the time you have available. The point of making an estimate now is so that you can begin to think of revision in realistic terms. It's no good hoping that you will somehow find time to re-read the whole course in detail. Once you can see roughly what time you have, you can divide it up between blocks and between different kinds of revision activity. Then you won't just start plodding through from Unit 1 and find that you've only reached half-way through the course when the exam is upon you. Your time is too precious to use haphazardly – you need to allocate it strategically.

5.3 Writing skills

Now we return to your essay-writing skills. This section looks first at one of the trickiest aspects of writing at degree level, which is developing an argument and drawing on evidence. Then it explores the similarities and differences between the kind of writing you are doing for your K100 essays and the report writing you might be required to do in a work setting.

Argument and evidence

The reason you write essays for K100 is to help you make the ideas and information you have been studying part of your own mental apparatus – not just something you have read about, but something you can use for yourself. You do this by weaving them together in an argument, written in a way that is convincing to a reader.

Study skills: Learning by arguing

'Speaking' your own thoughts (based on the key ideas you have been reading about) in the form of written sentences which lead logically from one to the next is perhaps the deepest form of learning on this kind of course. That is why your tutor gives attention to whether your arguments make sense and are backed up by evidence. It is a way of helping you to get to the heart of learning the course. To remind yourself what is meant by 'a coherent argument', quickly re-read Sections 3.4 and 3.5 of Chapter 5 of *The Good Study Guide*.

Grasping the general idea of what 'arguing a case' means is one thing. Being able to do it well is another. It involves developing a range of subtle insights and skills. These are explored in Chapter 6 of *The Good Study Guide*.

Activity 17 **Developing a convincing argument**

Allow about 1 hour

(a) Write 'Developing a convincing argument' at the head of a sheet of paper. Then read Section 5 of Chapter 6 of *The Good Study Guide*. As you read, write the sub-headings, sub-sub-headings and the key points (in brief) down the left-hand side of the sheet.

(b) You have written five essays for K100 (including TMA 07), and had comments back from your tutor. Have you looked back over them recently to see how your writing has developed and whether there are any patterns and themes in the comments your tutor has made? Find your essays now and look through the comments written on them. Have your sheet of paper beside you and check whether any of the comments relate to the sub-headings. Where they do, write the TMA number against the heading, along with a brief note of the comment. Also, check whether your tutor's point makes sense to you in the light of what you have just read in *The Good Study Guide*.

(c) When you have finished, look back over your page of notes and review your progress in writing convincing arguments. Make a quick note of anything to look out for when writing TMA 05.

Comment How much you were able to write on your page depends, of course, on how your essay writing is developing and on your tutor's way of commenting. But whether you found a lot of links or just a few, this kind of 'reflective' exercise is very useful. It is always worth setting your own experience alongside the advice offered in *The Good Study Guide*. In this case it may have helped to draw together a range of points made by your tutor over several months. Or it may have shown that you are doing well with your arguments and that you should just carry on developing along the same lines.

Writing reports

You have seen why we keep asking you to write essays in K100. But how relevant are the skills you are developing to the kind of report writing you might have to do in a care situation? How different is a report from an essay? You have read a lot about reports in Block 5, but just to remind you of how varied reports can be, skim quickly back over Activity 13 in Unit 18 (the one with the five reports of Anita Binns's experience at the Adult Training Centre) and the reports you wrote for Activities 6 and 9 in this unit. Now back to how reports differ from essays.

Brevity

Often the most obvious difference is length. People generally have limited time for reading reports. They want the bare essentials for the purposes of the job in hand. A key skill of report writing is to express your points in as few words as possible.

Restricted focus

Reports are usually highly selective in terms of what is included and what left out. This is partly for brevity, but also for clarity (for example what decisions need to be taken) and because it is not appropriate to discuss some things in a professional context, perhaps for reasons of confidentiality or avoiding personal bias. As you saw in Activity 13 in Unit 18, reports of the same event can have very different focuses (in this case the person, the institution, and the process). None of the reports attempted to give a 'rounded' picture. They were addressed to particular concerns and ignored everything else. One of the hardest things when you are new to report writing is learning what you should leave out and what is essential to keep in. For example, if you have to write case notes about someone it is very easy to slip into a biographical style: 'telling the human story'; highlighting personalities, fateful moments and emotional upheavals, while not making clear exactly what problems the case is concerned with; or leaving out, or jumbling up, important details about times and places of treatments, and so on.

Specificity of purpose

The broad purposes of an essay (which tend to remain the same whatever course you study) are to help you explore ideas and to enable your progress to be assessed. The purposes of a report tend to be much more specific to a context. An institution 'requires' the report for a specific reason. Writing it is not an open, creative enterprise. The report has to meet criteria of usefulness and professional correctness. Everything that goes into it needs to be judged against these criteria. Understanding the particular purposes to which your reports will be put is an important part of developing skill in report writing.

Readership and voice

You write essays as one student of the subject presenting an argument to others who may be interested in it. By contrast you write a report as a person in a particular role. You 'speak' in the context of the responsibilities and status of that role. You also address your audience in terms of their role – whether they are clients, junior colleagues, senior colleagues, or members of another professional group. Both your own role and that of your audience determine what is an appropriate 'voice' and tone to adopt. The activity in Unit 18 shows this very clearly. You were probably able to make quite shrewd judgements about who the different versions could have been written by and who they might be written for. Growing into your own role and learning to relate to other people in their roles is an important part of developing an effective report-writing voice.

Activity 18   **Evaluating your own reports**

Allow about 10 minutes   Activities 6 and 9 in this unit asked you to write reports. This activity asks you to evaluate one or both of them in terms of what you have just read about report writing. Read either or both reports again, reminding yourself who the report was intended for, and answer the two following questions.

(a)   Did the report tell your readers all they needed to know using as few words as possible?

(b)   Did the report tell your readers anything they didn't need to know (including anything they didn't have a right to know)?

Comment   You will probably have guessed that if your answer to question (a) was 'yes' and your answer to question (b) was 'no', then your report will have shown the characteristics of brevity, restricted focus and specificity of purpose, and, of course, you will have written a report to meet the needs of its intended readers. If you can work out what the readers of a report need to know, then everything else falls into place.

If you are going to include either of these reports in a portfolio, it would probably be a good idea now to do some editing: putting in anything you have left out which the readers of the report needed to know, and cutting out anything extra.

Skills of report writing

These, then, are some of the main differences between reports and essays. But how different are the skills you need in writing a report? As you have seen, a lot depends on the particular context in which the report is written. Many of the key skills can be fully developed only in a practical situation, where you have a specific role to play and a specific audience to write to. Often reports use a kind of institutional shorthand. They follow a format and style that other reports have used before, so that colleagues know what to look for and where. Instead of spelling things out in full, the writer assumes that colleagues will use their experience to fill in the gaps. To write good reports takes practice in learning the format and style of the particular setting within which you are reporting.

An appropriate format for a report will vary from agency to agency and situation to situation. However, in the context of an OU course, you might write a report, say, on a project you have undertaken. This would be longer and contain more discussion than most work-related reports such as those you wrote for Activities 6 and 9, but it would still be distinctly different from an essay. A major difference is that usually you will be required to organise the report into sections, each with a particular job to do and with its own particular style. Here is a typical structure for a project report.

Introduction. This is an outline of the question(s) the project is investigating and why, making very brief reference back to other studies in the field, to show what your approach is based on. There are no grand claims, no persuasive or emotive flourishes, just sufficient argument to set a framework for what follows (about a paragraph).

Method. This is an outline of why you chose the particular way of gathering information that you did; what you saw as the advantages of this approach as well as what it might leave out; followed by a factual description of the main elements of the investigation, from the early pilot stages to the main data gathering (for example, how many people you interviewed, how you selected them, where you interviewed them, how long for, whether you followed a standard pattern of questions), along with anything that didn't go according to plan and might have influenced the outcome. The style of this section should be as pared down as possible – dry, objective, 'technical', almost like a set of instructions for someone who might want to repeat your study. The length can vary depending on the subtlety of your 'methodology' (your method of enquiry and the assumptions on which it rests), but it could be as little as a page.

Findings. This is often a very challenging section to write because you have to work out how to summarise briefly and simply a lot of very varied information. If you have carried out interviews it might involve quite a lengthy summary of the main types of answer given, including sample quotations. However, if you have used a questionnaire, the section might consist mainly of a table of results. The essence of this section is that it does *not* include any *discussion* of what the findings mean. The aim is to present objective, unvarnished data that stand alone. It should be possible for someone who disagrees with your point of view to read your findings and use them to draw different conclusions.

Discussion. Here you discuss various ways in which the findings might be interpreted. You link them back to the framework for the investigation which you set up in the introduction. And you consider what influences your method might have had on the results. This section is the most like an ordinary essay.

Conclusion. This is a very brief summary of what you set out to investigate and the main conclusions you think can be drawn.

As you can see, a report of this kind involves some very different forms of writing from the discursive essay style. Much of the report is plain, simple, pared-down writing, which aims for objective, accurate description rather than discussion. It takes some practice to develop a polished reporting style, but it isn't a skill on the same scale as learning to write arguments in essays. It doesn't require you to develop a whole new way of thinking and working over a period of several months. It's more a matter of knocking the flourishes off your normal style and fitting into an established framework.

However, beneath the more formal descriptive elements of the report lies (guess what) an argument. It surfaces briefly in the introduction and conclusion and rather more fully in the discussion. It is this argument that holds the report together and gives it strength. So arguing is still a key skill, even though it isn't in evidence at every point in the document. To this extent the skills you develop through your TMAs are highly generalisable. Once you can handle arguments comfortably you can quite quickly become effective in many other kinds of writing.

Study skills: Transferability of arguing skills

The skills which you are developing through essay writing – of arguing a case from evidence – are actually highly relevant to other forms of writing such as report writing. Essays bring the arguing side of writing into the spotlight, making it possible for your tutor to 'coach' you in getting your arguments right. But other forms of writing also present arguments, although often in a more hidden way. As you saw in Unit 18, although reports *look* very different from essays, there is almost always an underlying *purpose* to what is said. In other words a report usually presents an underlying argument of some kind. The terms of the argument are not usually spelt out. In fact, they tend to be assumed as 'obvious', given the circumstances in which the report is written and the audience who will read it. Nevertheless, the writer's basic skill in putting together a convincing case is what gives a report force. The more you develop your techniques of arguing, the better you will be able to select just the few elements you need to deliver punchy reports.

End of block assignment

Now you have another chance to develop your skills of arguing as you write TMA 05. Your review of your previous essays should help here.

Study skills: Study diary

Just a reminder to bring your study diary up to date, to help you think ahead to Block 6.

References

Audit Commission (1994) *Finding a Place: A Review of Mental Health Services for Adults*, HMSO, London.

CCETSW/City and Guilds of London Institute (1997) *Draft Revised Standards: Care Level 3*, Joint Awarding Bodies (CCETSW and City and Guilds), London.

United Kingdom Council for Nurses, Midwives and Health Visitors (1992) *Professional Code of Conduct*, UKCC, London.

United Kingdom Council for Nurses, Midwives and Health Visitors (1996) *Guidelines for Professional Practice*, UKCC, London.

Acknowledgements

Grateful acknowledgement is made to the following source for permission to reproduce material in this unit:

Figure 2: Audit Commission (1994) *Finding a Place: A Review of Mental Health Services for Adults*.

Grateful acknowledgement is made to the following sources for permission to reproduce the illustrations on the front cover of this block: all Sally and Richard Greenhill except *top right* Brenda Prince/Format and *bottom right* John Birdsall Photography.